125 Years of Indiana Pharmacy:
A History of Indiana's Pharmacist Association

written by
David A. Zahl

A publication of the
Indiana Pharmacists Alliance
Indianapolis, Indiana

Indiana Pharmacists Alliance
729 N. Pennsylvania Street
Indianapolis, IN 46204
(317) 634-4968
www.indianapharmacists.org

In association with
IBJ Custom Publishing
41 E. Washington Street, Suite 200
Indianapolis, IN 46204
www.ibjcustompublishing.com

David A. Zahl
    125 Years of Indiana Pharmacy: A History of Indiana's Pharmacist Association

ISBN 978-0-9776675-9-8

Table of Contents

Foreword

I t's a very difficult thing to condense 125 years of history into a relatively short narrative. There are many decisions to make. What do you put in, what do you leave out, how do you get all of the details into a single book? Well, as we found out, you can't put everything into a short book with a deadline looming. It was not possible to chronicle the actions and activities of the entire history of the association. We decided to focus on the effects that the association had on the profession of pharmacy in the state, and how it affected the public health and safety of Indiana's citizens. Consequently, much of the discussion in the book is related to the larger issues of the day such as legislative initiatives, public health issues, and the role of the association in molding the profession of pharmacy within the state of Indiana.

Our thanks go to several people and organizations for their help in getting this book into print and into the hands of the pharmacists of Indiana. First, we owe much to the Hooks Drug Foundation and the Pharmacy Education Foundation for their most generous support of our efforts to get this project off the ground. Both of these Foundations provided the initial financial support for our efforts. Thank you both for your faith in our vision and your support. Your help enabled us to contract with Indiana University-Purdue University Indianapolis for the services of a writer to actually do the research and write this book.

Support for the publication and distribution of this book is a matter of the arc of the association's history coming full circle. In 1882, one of the pharmacists who was instrumental in calling the organizing convention together and leading the meeting that created the IPhA was Col. Eli Lilly. Mr. Lilly was an active member of the association for many years, as was his son Josiah. The Lillys and the company were always ready to provide support, monetary, moral and otherwise to the association during its early years, and indeed throughout the association's existence. And once again, Lilly has stepped up to support the organization. Eli Lilly & Co. has been most generous in providing us with resources to print and distribute this history. The Alliance extends our thanks to John Poulin and the Eli Lilly Company for their assistance in celebrating the 125th birthday of this organization. They were there at the beginning, and the tradition is continuing 125 years later.

I need to say a word about the author of this book. David Zahl has turned out to be a great choice to write this book. I know that he spent many hours researching the book at our office, the Indiana Historical Society and any other place where he thought there might be a document that would be helpful. He has a passionate interest in history, and in this instance, the history of the association. I think that the IPA is extremely fortunate to have gotten David to author our history, and I'm sure you will enjoy reading David's story of the IPA, or as it was originally known, the IPhA. Thanks David for all of your hard work on this book.

We owe a special thanks to Dr. Bruce Clayton, for his help in editing the many drafts of the material for the book, and thanks to Tabitha Cross, the managing editor of all of our publications, for her attention to detail and deadlines.

Finally, thanks to all of those pharmacists who have gone before. To all of those men and women who gave of their time, their treasure, and their passion, to create, nurture and grow the professional organization for pharmacists in Indiana. As is true in any volunteer organization, the association is only as strong as its' members. Throughout it's history, first as the Indiana Pharmaceutical Association, then the Indiana Pharmacists Association and the Indiana Society of Hospital Pharmacists, and now today, the Indiana Pharmacists Alliance, the association has been blessed with the services of generations of caring pharmacists. Congratulations and Happy Birthday.

Lawrence J. Sage, B.A., M.P.A.
Executive Vice President
Indiana Pharmacists Alliance

For Jim and Shirley Garoutte

Author's Acknowledgements

I would like to start by congratulating the members of the Indiana Pharmacists Alliance on 125 years of serving Hoosier pharmacists. Two and a half months of research and writing are not enough to give justice to your fine organization. I do hope that this book provides a glimpse into some of the people, events, and actions that helped shape the development of your association. I thoroughly enjoyed researching and writing every chapter and hope that my enthusiasm is reflected in the text. This work is by no means meant to be exhaustive and despite my earnest efforts, I am sure that there are shortcomings and omissions. However, if it can serve as a baseline to cultivate future reading, writing, and discussion about the history of the IPA, I will consider it a great success.

The efforts involved in seeing this book come to fruition were not mine alone and I would like to thank all those that contributed. To Lary Sage, Tabitha Cross, and Philip Scarpino, I would like to thank you for giving me the opportunity to work on this project. Lary and Tabitha went to great lengths to provide an amicable research environment and were always eager to lend a helping hand. I would like to thank Bruce Clayton for his valuable comments on drafts and for our discussions about the history of the IPA. The students at Butler are lucky to have a professor of your quality. I would like to issue a special thanks to William Schneider for being a friend and mentor to me over the past year. Your insight and guidance during the project was invaluable and I would not have been able to do it without you. To Sarah, I would like to share a sigh of relief; thank you for all of your encouragement and always lending a sympathetic ear, a reassuring smile, and heartfelt advice. Most importantly I would like to thank Mom, Dad, and Calyn for all of their love and support. Everything I am and do is because of you.

Founding of the Indiana Pharmaceutical Association

On the evening of Monday, May 8, 1882 a group of pharmacists from across the state of Indiana met in the Bates House parlors in Indianapolis. City and small town druggists alike exchanged pleasantries and engaged in conversation to pass the evening. These men, earnest in their conviction, had come to Indianapolis with the purpose of meeting the following day to establish a State Association of Pharmacy.

In years prior, there had been clamoring from city associations about the need for such an organization. In the recent memory of the druggists of Indianapolis, a motion for such an establishment was "quietly canvassed" during a winter meeting in 1881. It was thought, however, that a convention was necessary for establishing something so important. The druggists of Indianapolis who met the following winter played a substantial role in organizing Indiana pharmacists and the convention they thought necessary for the task. The group of pharmacists who met at the Bates House parlors had come at the request of the druggists to participate in what would be the founding meeting of the Indiana Pharmaceutical Association. The convention on May 9, 1882 was where Hoosier pharmacists finally united under a single banner.

The Necessary Preparations

One of the druggists of Indianapolis who played a prominent role in organizing the May 9th convention was Joseph R. Perry. While the issue of establishing a state association had been supported by many of the pharmacists in Indiana, the issue had garnered little widespread support because of the profession's desire to avoid any associated prominence. Following the winter meeting of the druggists of Indianapolis, Joseph Perry acknowledged that it was time for pharmacy to establish professional prominence within the state. On January 24, 1882, Perry mailed a postcard to all active Indiana members of the

---

INDIANAPOLIS, January 24, 1882.

" DEAR SIR : It is desirable that there be a State Pharmaceutical Association in Indiana. As a member of the A. P. A., may I affix your name to a call for a meeting next May, to organize such Association?

Very truly yours, JOS. R. PERRY."

Call for organizational meeting, January 24, 1882

American Pharmaceutical Association to gauge interest in establishing a state association. All who responded to the initial inquiry favored the idea and Perry sent out a second mailing, including the names of individual supporters and inviting Hoosier pharmacists to participate in the organization of the Indiana Pharmaceutical Association.

Dear Sir: It is desirable that there be a State Pharmaceutical Association in Indiana. The reasons why this is desirable are so numerous and so weighty that to mention them would seem superfluous. Our sister States, Ohio, Michigan, Illinois and Kentucky, each have flourishing Associations, also Pharmacy Laws, regulating the profession. We need all these adjuncts in this State tending to elevate our business. For the purpose of accomplishing some of these worthy objects, it has been deemed advisable to call a meeting of the druggists of Indiana, to be held in Indianapolis on Tuesday, May 9, 1882. You are cordially invited, and earnestly requested, to be present at that time, and give your assistance and aid in effecting the organization of the Indiana Pharmaceutical Association.

Fraternally yours,

A.B. Buck, Anderson.	A.H. Hatfield, New Albany.	Geo. W. Sloan, Indianapolis.
J.C. Brandon, Anderson.	August Knoefel, NewAlbany.	Henry Schraeder, Indianapolis.
G. D. Searle, Anderson.	J. H. Andrews, Seymour.	
H.J. Marshall, Aurora.	Jacob Bauer, Terre Haute.	Jos. R. Perry, Indianapolis.
H.J. Schlaepfer, Evansville.	W.C. Buntin, Terre Haute.	L.H. Mueller, Indianapolis.
Jas. A. Riddle, Aurora.	August Schreiber, Tell City.	Chas. E. Miller, Indianapolis.
John C. Loomis, Jeffersonville.	Herman Frauer, Indianapolis.	Emil Martin, Indianapolis.
W.A. Irvin, Kokomo.	Chas. Beyschlag, Indianapolis.	John A. Lambert, Indianapolis.
David Hilt, Lafayette.	N.S. Driggs, Indianapolis.	Henry Kielhorn, Indianapolis.
N.W. Yeakle, Lafayette.	M. Staley, Indianapolis.	
C.E. Ferris, Lawrenceburg.	Jos. Earnshaw, Indianapolis.	Julius A. Haag, Indianapolis.
F.M. Harper, Madison.	Arthur Timberlake, Indianapolis	J.B. Dill, Indianapolis.
J.S. Connor, New Albany.		

Please let us know if you will be present so that we can make arrangements with the railroads and hotels for reduced rates. Communications may be addressed to[:] Jos. R. Perry, 502 E. Washington St., Indianapolis, Ind.[2]

Within days, Perry received over 300 responses, all of which expressed ardent enthusiasm for the charge in his circular. Confident that the meeting would come to fruition, the druggists of Indianapolis formed committees to greet their guests, provide entertainment, and reduce the rates of railroad fares and hotel prices. With the arrangements made, Perry mailed a third circular on April 14, 1882 to inform his fellow professionals of the travel and lodging accommodations, the place and time of the meeting, and the use of the Bates House as a headquarters for the event. In response to the mailing, over 350 druggists requested the reduced fare certificates and indicated their support for the event. Encouraged by the favorable responses, the druggists of Indianapolis were optimistic about the May 9th meeting.

The First Meeting of the Indiana Pharmaceutical Association

The rain and clouds on the morning of May 9, 1882 failed to deter the 120 pharmacists who were ushered into Indianapolis Masonic Temple for the meeting. Expecting more than 300 guests, the low attendance was attributed to a change in the scheduling of a State Medical Association meeting the same day. For fear that a community would be without both a physician and a pharmacist, many of the interested individuals thought it their duty to remain at home in case of an emergency. At 10:30 AM, Joseph Perry called those in attendance to order and stated the task before them. "We are here this morning for the purpose of organizing a State Pharmaceutical Association, that we, as druggists, may better our condition".[3]

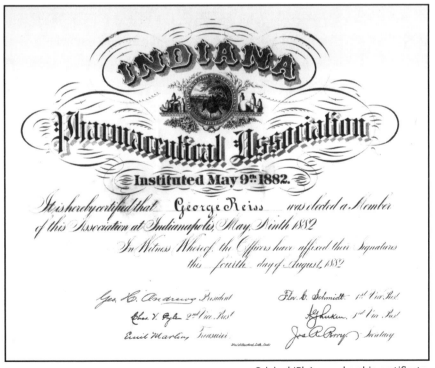

Original IPhA membership certificate.

One can imagine how each man in the Masonic Temple understood the term 'condition' and the necessary actions to improve the status of the profession. The pharmacists soon found that the ambiguity of Perry's term 'condition' became more lucid as the proceedings developed, and that its improvement was dependent on key issues common to most Hoosier pharmacists. In addition to the business of founding a state association, the first meeting of the Indiana Pharmaceutical Association served as a forum for the pharmacists to communicate with one another. A pharmacist was able to share with his colleagues individual concerns and, in turn, the group was able to assess the current state of the profession as a whole. Many of the issues identified by individuals became rallying points for the entire association. In particular, the manner by which legislation would be drafted and presented, the use of patent medicines, professional standards and ethics, and the scope of the organization were all matters addressed during the proceedings of the first annual meeting.

Following Perry's address and a prayer by Reverend Edward A. Bradley, the business of founding the State Association commenced. The first order was to elect a temporary chairman for the proceedings until permanent officers were elected later in the meeting. John Newell Hurty of Indianapolis nominated W.C. Buntin of Terre Haute for the position and the motion was unanimously passed. Shortly after, Joseph Perry was unanimously elected as the temporary secretary. Both men humbly accepted their positions and asserted they would do their earnest best until permanent positions were voted on. Following the appointment of the two temporary positions, Colonel Eli Lilly of Indianapolis motioned that a committee of five be appointed to draft the permanent organization of the association. The men appointed to the committee were Lilly, H.J. Watjen of Vincennes, A. M. Andrews of Connersville, A.K. Plank of Rochester, and A.G. Luken of Richmond. The committee was charged with drafting a constitution and by-laws for the governance of the Association and nominating individuals for permanent positions.

The Committee on Permanent Organization drafted a constitution and by-laws to present before the organization during the afternoon session of the first day. Few amendments were needed to the original draft and after reading and adopting all the articles of the constitution and by-laws, all 120 men in attendance signed the document. The nominees for permanent positions in the organization that the committee supported were as follows:

President – Geo. H. Andrews, Muncie
First Vice President – Flor. C. Schmidt, Evansville
Second Vice President – Charles V. Pyle, Warsaw
Third Vice President – A.G. Luken, Richmond
Permanent Secretary – Joseph R. Perry, Indianapolis
Local Secretary – John A. Lambert, Indianapolis
Treasurer – Emil Martin
Executive Committee – Jacob Baur, Terre Haute; John N. Hurty, Indianapolis; David Hilt, Lafeyette
Delegates to the American Pharmaceutical Association Meeting at Niagara Falls – George W. Sloan, Indianapolis; Leo Eliel, South Bend; R. C. Knoefel, Rensselaer; H.J. Watjen, Vincennes[4]

Perry presided over the balloting, and all of the nominees were elected. The constitution, by-laws, and elected officers provided a foundation of solidarity and legitimacy for the members of the association. With the permanent organization approved by the 120 members present at the meeting, the Indiana Pharmaceutical Association became Indiana's newest professional organization.

A Need for Effective Legislation

The nascent association addressed many issues during the two-day proceedings, among the first was the need to procure effective legislation for the profession. Nearly ubiquitous among druggists from every region in the State, this issue was first addressed at the proceedings following a letter written by W.L. Johnston, President of the Evansville Pharmaceutical Association. In his letter, Johnston enumerated the ways in which legislation in other states had been ineffective and counterproductive to the efforts of the pharmacist. The underlying reason for the problematic legislation was the haste taken in securing the enactment of the laws. His charge to the Indiana Pharmaceutical Association was to avoid hasty action and appoint a committee to read all existing pharmaceutical legislation, incorporate the beneficial aspects, and avoid the mistakes of other States

To assist with enforcement of laws, Johnston proposed that the first duty of the legislative committee should be to draft an "'Act of Incorporation of the Indiana Pharmaceutical Association,' giving the Association all the powers usually granted to bodies corporate."[5] In this capacity, the Association could bolster the power of a Board of Pharmacy in enforcing pharmaceutical laws. Johnston's letter outlined a prudent course of action to draft and enforce legislation. The individuals at the meeting rallied around Johnston's letter. George Sloan of Indianapolis reiterated Johnston's desire to avoid undue haste stating that a "poor law is worse than no law at all."[6] Sloan expounded on Johnston's recommendation and motioned that a drafted law should be sent to all members of the Association to share with friends, customers, and patrons. Members of the community would then have the opportunity to read the legislation and sign a petition for its enactment into law. The Association was mindful of political procedure and a petition for legislation would serve a dual purpose. Members of the community would be better informed of the Association's efforts, and in turn the Association would have political leverage when dealing with the Legislature. The legislation would not just be for the pharmacist, but also for the people. Sloan's motion prevailed and on the second day of the meeting a committee was appointed on Legislative and Trade Interest. The members included Chairman Aug. Detzer of Fort Wayne, F.C. Schmidt of Evansville, J.E. Somes of Terre Haute, Henry Kielhorn of Indianapolis, and Leo Eliel of South Bend. By recommendation of President Andrews, the committee was to meet once a year outside of the annual meeting and follow the recommendations of Johnston and Sloan.

One need for legislation was to safeguard the profession from "knaves and mountebancks" who preyed on uninformed consumers.[7] An anecdote printed in the first issue of *The Indiana Pharmacist* – the publication of the Indiana Pharmaceutical Association– recounted one such instance. A Reverend Joseph T. Inman of Station D, Bible House New York was a pseudonym used by an individual advertising a cure for tuberculosis, commonly referred to as consumption, in religious papers throughout the country. The guise of a Reverend advertising a medical cure in religious papers preyed on the faith of the religious journal's readers. The mailing address too was a ruse; Station D, Bible House was a regular branch of the post office located in the Bible Society's building in New York.[8] Individuals afflicted with consumption sent money for the prescription and got a list of ingredients to take to their local pharmacist. When the pharmacists attempted to fill the prescription, they realized that it contained fictional items and was utterly useless. Upon hearing that their prescription was useless and that Rev. Inman was indeed a quack, the patron would disagree with the pharmacist, citing the religious publication where they found the advertisement. The patron would then be forced to send an immoderate sum to Rev. Inman for the cure. Not only did the patron have to pay for the prescription, they also had to pay Rev. Inman to compound the medicine.

Establishing the Aim of the Association

Situations such as the artifice of Reverend Joseph T. Inman demonstrated the need for professional standards and ethics within the profession of pharmacy and the need for legislation to enforce the ethics of the profession. The first annual meeting, whether directly or indirectly, was a forum to restate the professional standards and ethics that were the crux of the profession. Hoosier pharmacists thought that their success was determined by their knowledge, skill, and integrity.[9] They had a deep sense of personal responsibility towards their patrons and the physician. Responsibility meant not only meticulously filling prescriptions but also making sure that the prescription was written correctly by the physician. According to *The Indiana Pharmacist*, the Hoosier pharmacist was a neat, agile, and pleasant man that treated each costumer with deference independent of social class or intelligence. Their knowledge, skill, and agility were necessary for filling the myriad prescriptions that they encountered and their integrity and pleasant demeanor secured repeat patronage. The balancing of scientific professionalism and business savvy was a challenge for Hoosier pharmacists which continued throughout the history of pharmacy in Indiana.

The members of the Indiana Pharmaceutical Association restated their commitment to professional standards and ethics when the 120 members present signed their names approving the constitution. Article II stated the objective of the organization and demonstrated their commitment to professionalism and their mindfulness of business matters.

Article II

Object.

The aim of this Association shall be to unite all reputable druggists and apothecaries of the State for mutual encouragement and assistance; in improving the existing methods of pharmacy, by disseminating the latest discoveries in our art, thereby stimulating to further discoveries and inventions; to establish closer and more cordial relations between pharmacists, physicians and the public at large, whereby we may promote the general welfare and tend to the mutual advantage of all; to discourage, within due limits, unwise competition in our own ranks, and to devise means to prevent our lawful profits being taken by those outside of our profession engaged simply in mercantile pursuits; to elevate the standard of our profession; and ultimately to restrain the practice of pharmacy to properly qualified druggists and apothecaries.[10]

The Concern with Patent Medicines

Connected to the issue of professional standards and ethics was the concern with the influx of patent medicines in the pharmacy. Patent medicines were highly advertised remedies with trademarked names, secret ingredients, and questionable efficacy. Pharmacists were often conflicted about purchasing and dispensing patents. In some ways patents were a blessing for business. Advertisements created notoriety for the remedies and the ready-made mixtures were easily dispensed by the pharmacist. Other pharmacists maintained that they had the skill to create similar compounds of a higher quality that would cost less to make and could be sold for more profit. George Sloan first brought the issue before the Association while reading his paper entitled "Then and Now" during the second day of the proceedings. Sloan compared the pharmacy of the 1850's to the pharmacy of the 1880's highlighting the differences in the preparation of medicines, the role of the apprentice, the duties of the pharmacist, the types of medicinal items carried, and the working day. One of the differences highlighted in his paper was the use of patent medicines. A prescription from a physician calling for a specific patent medicine was to be filled exactly as the prescription stated even if the pharmacist had the ability to create his own similar mixture. Often times, physicians were told of the ingredients within the medicine by the manufacturer while the pharmacist was devoid of the information. Sloan mused in his paper: "Now where remains the need for study or education upon the part of the Pharmacist of the times?"[11] Sloan asserted that it was the duty of Hoosier pharmacists to be fully knowledgeable and capable to perform the art of his trade. A knowledgeable and capable pharmacist would not only garner the confidence of the patron but also the respect and trust of the physician to allow the pharmacist to use their own mixtures. Sloan's paper provides an excellent commentary on the state of pharmaceutical education in Indiana. While education was not addressed during these first proceedings, the standardization of pharmacy education would be a reoccurring issue in the years to come.

Following Sloan's paper, August J. Detzer of Fort Wayne submitted a resolution stating that the "trade-marked and copy-righted medicines, introduced into our profession, are detrimental and objectionable to the Pharmaceutical profession".[12] The resolution was seconded by Mr. Cowdrey, a pharmacist attending from Chicago, IL. Cowdrey shared a paper written by Dr. N.J. Davis, a physician from Chicago, questioning the ethics of physicians that prescribe patent medicines. The paper asserted that it was the ethical obligation of the physician to abstain from prescribing patent medicines. It was contradictory to the code of ethics of physicians and pharmacists to prescribe medicines in which the formulas of the constituents were unknown. Professional ethics dictated that the physician and the pharmacist combine their knowledge to create a medicine tailored to the needs of the patient. According to Davis, it was the duty of the physician to ascertain the correct proportions and types of ingredients and the duty of the pharmacist to correctly create the compound prescribed by the physician. Under these professional guidelines, prescribing a medicine of unknown quantity and substance is morally reprehensible to both the physician and the pharmacist. Following Cowdrey's reading and commitments, Detzer's resolution was adopted.

The Scope of the IPhA

The history of pharmacy in Indiana has seen many battles between pharmacists whose livelihood depended on different facets of the profession. During the proceedings, a concern for the scope of the organization was raised by S.J. Barrett of Columbus. Stating that retail pharmacists were excluded from the wholesale druggists convention, Barrett asserted that the governing body of the Association should be comprised exclusively of retail druggists and that bettering the condition of retail pharmacy should be its primary endeavor. Both W.C. Buntin and Jacob Baur quickly disagreed with Barrett's remarks. Buntin challenged that the call for convention did not read "'Retail Druggists' or 'Wholesale Druggists,' but 'The Druggists of Indiana.'"[13] Baur added that "it matters not whether they are retail, wholesale, or traveling men, so they have served an apprenticeship and have the interests of business at heart, and are thorough pharmacists."[14]

The critics of wholesale druggists were silenced only momentarily. During adoption of the constitution an amendment was proposed by Mr. Dill of Indianapolis stating: "No manufacturing Pharmacist, wholesale druggist, proprietor or manufacturer of any secret nostrum or patent medicine shall be eligible to hold office in this Association."[15] With the words of Buntin and Baur still palpable within the hall, the amendment garnered little support and was withdrawn. The proceedings of the first annual meeting were important in establishing the scope of the Indiana Pharmaceutical Association as an organization to unify all Hoosier pharmacists. A fractured association or an association supporting only one facet of pharmacy in Indiana would have had substantially less power than one embracing all facets.

Conclusion

The First Annual Meeting of the Indiana Pharmaceutical Association was a large success and an important step in the professionalization of pharmacy in Indiana. During the proceedings, letters from other State Associations were read that shared support for the Hoosier pharmacists and appreciation for undertaking such a large task. Support was also given by Mayor Grubbs of Indianapolis and Governor A.G. Porter of Indiana. Both men spoke at the convention and conveyed their earnest gratitude for the efforts of the men and their vision for the future of pharmacy in Indiana.

The men who met at the Masonic Temple on May 9th and 10th left with a much better idea of what bettering the 'condition' of pharmacy meant to them and to the profession as a whole. The issues of legislation, scope of the organization, and professional standards and ethics was often revisited in subsequent years. The pharmacists that attended the meeting established a firm foundation to build the profession of pharmacy in Indiana and set important precedents for future pharmacists to follow. Most importantly, they accomplished the task before them, founding the Indiana Pharmaceutical Association uniting all Hoosier Pharmacists.

Section 1 Endnotes

[1] *Proceedings of the Indiana Pharmaceutical Association,* Frank H. Smith, Printer: Indianapolis (1882), 5.

[2] Ibid., 6.

[3] Ibid., 18.

[4] Ibid., 23.

[5] Ibid., 16.

[6] Ibid., 25.

[7] Ibid., 15.

[8] "A Medical Humbug", *The Indiana Pharmacist* 1, no. 1 (1882): 3.

[9] Ibid., 1.

[10] *Proceedings of the Indiana Pharmaceutical Association,* 45.

[11] Ibid., 32.

[12] Ibid., 35.

[13] Ibid., 13.

[14] Ibid., 13.

[15] Ibid., 13.

*Hoosier
Pharmacy
during the
Progressive Era*

[Editor's Note: *The Indiana Pharmacist* was not published from 1894 to 1918. Important events including passage of the Harrison Narcotic Act (1914), the Spanish Flu Epidemic (1918), and World War I (1914-1918) took place during this gap between journals. Meeting proceedings for these years were also unavailable making it difficult to determine the IPhA's specific involvement.]

"Pharmacy is a progressive science."1 Thus, did August J. Detzer of Fort Wayne posit the nature of Hoosier pharmacy in his presidential address during the fifth annual meeting of the Indiana Pharmaceutical Association in 1886? For the pharmacists living during this time in American History, progress was a term used to describe the possibility to better the situation of an individual, group, and society as a whole. For the historian, the progressive era was a period of great transformation that influenced the praxis of the nation for the following decades. This was a multifaceted period in American History typified by the formation of reform groups, a general concern for the livelihood of American society, and the balance of strong government intervention with respect for individual and State liberties. Thus growth and progress of the Indiana Pharmaceutical Association, at this time was part of the great changes that were taking place across the nation. The Indiana Pharmaceutical Association (IPhA), like many other associations during the progressive era, made great strides between the years of 1893-1918, to advance pharmacy education in the state, pass the first pharmacy legislation, and establish a State Board of Pharmacy.

The Depression of 1890

Many historians have noted the national depression from 1890 - 1894 as the beginning of the progressive era. Pharmacy in Indiana was not immune to the economic doldrums of this time and indeed, could be considered one of the first professions affected by the depression. As early as 1884, President Nathan W. Yeakel described the economic hardships of both manufacturing drug companies and retail pharmacists having to close shop because of financial ruin. His words were reiterated in 1886 by Detzer in his presidential address stating that the "general stagnation in business has kept pace in the past year with that of former years".2 While both men mentioned one reason for the situation was that the population had been relatively healthy over the past years, but in hindsight it is also because individuals simply had less money to spend. With Hoosier pharmacy still developing as a profession and raising standards, many individuals may have sought other, less expensive means to remedy the maladies that plagued the family. Even though Yeakel and Detzer mentioned the overall health of the population as a contributor to the economic hardships of pharmacy, they both pointed accusatory fingers at what they believed was the continuing culprit – patent medicine.

IPhA journal advertisements for patent medicine.

Patent medicines were purchased at a premium price by retail pharmacists. Consequently, there was very little, if any, profit associated with selling such items to a public that generally could not afford them. The practice of "cutting" or "cutting rates" caused competition within the ranks of retail pharmacy. A pharmacist, knowing that the general public could not afford patent medicines, would sell the remedies for little or no profit in an effort to cultivate repeat patronage. Pharmacists that chose not to cut the prices of their patent medicines would lose business to the rival drug store that had a reputation for lower prices. In actuality, the only ones benefiting from the situation was the wholesale distributors and of course, the owners of the patents. Both Yeakel and Detzer attributed the sale of the remedies to either laziness or ignorance of the retail pharmacist to create their own medicines. Furthermore, physicians would prescribe the medicines by name and it was considered unethical to substitute one's own mixture for the patent. It was encouraged, however, to abstain from using the patents and instead to create one's own mixture when a patron asked for the remedy for a general ailment. This practice not only bolstered the financial situation of the pharmacist, but also increased his or her reputation as a knowledgeable professional.

The depression of the 1890's ended in 1896 with the discovery of gold in South Africa and the Canadian Yukon.[3] Since its effects came earlier to Indiana, the national depression was in actuality a twelve year drought in business for Hoosier pharmacists. The depression challenged the business savvy of many pharmacists and the competition from patent medicine nostrums and other charlatans compounded the situation. The treasury of the IPhA was in such straits between the years of 1886 and 1888 that the proceedings of the annual meeting were not printed and distributed to the members as in years past. Even though the economy grew following 1896 and individuals had more money to spend, the problem of patent medicines and price cutting continued. Along with these problems, the presidential addresses of Yeakel and Detzer outlined other challenges for the IPhA for the next three decades. Both men spoke extensively about the need for pharmacy legislation, the importance of educating future pharmacists, and the profession's precarious position with physicians.

The Seventeen Year War: Enacting Legislation in Indiana

From the inception of the IPhA in 1882 it was the intention of Hoosier pharmacists to pass legislation to protect and elevate the profession. What initially began as a forthright process became an arduous seventeen year war of attrition, the most striking feature about passage of Indiana's first pharmacy law was the sheer length of time it required. When it finally was passed, all four neighboring states had pharmacy laws prior to Indiana.

The first attempt to pass a pharmacy law was during the 1883 legislative session. The IPhA's Committee on Legislative and Trade Interest, comprised of Chairman August J. Detzer, F.C. Schmidt of Evansville, J.E. Somes of Terre Haute, Henry Kielhorn of Indianapolis, and Leo Eliel of South Bend, drafted a law for the association and proposed the bill to the legislature. Leo Eliel read

Chairman Detzer's report during the IPhA Annual meeting in 1883:

> All are aware that the proposed Pharmacy Law died a short time after its birth, nestling in the arms of entrusted servants, who were to instill into it life and vigor and rear it to maturity, but alas, simply for the want of "soothing syrup," its little life flickered out, notwithstanding the restoratives that were employed in the way of encouragement to sustain its precious life. Know ye all, that the proper panacea for legislation is "soothing syrup."

As Detzer so eloquently wrote, the "Pharmacy Law died a short time after its birth". This was the first of many setbacks for the supporters of pharmacy legislation in Indiana. The task to procure legislation required many caretakers; both Detzer and Eliel were staunch supporters of a pharmacy law and worked fervently for the cause.

Following another defeat in the Legislature in 1885, it was apparent to the individuals of the association that members of the retail drug trade posed the greatest opposition to the bill. During the annual meeting of 1886, Leo Eliel called an optional meeting at 8:30 PM on July 9th, the evening of the second day of proceedings, to discuss the procurement of the pharmacy law in the 1887 legislative session.[4] It was the consensus of the gentlemen present that many of the retail pharmacists who opposed the law did so due to a misunderstanding that they and their clerks would have to pass examinations before conducting further business. The individuals present reread the provisions of the law and were satisfied that the language was appropriate and that no such claims were made.

Eliel and the others at the evening meeting were correct in their assessment of the opposition posed by some of the retail druggists. An article submitted to the association's monthly publication, *The Indiana Pharmacist* in 1886, by a concerned retail pharmacist posed several questions including examinations for current pharmacists and clerks, increased salary for clerks, and the presumed power of the State Board of Pharmacy. Other pharmacists submitted letters claiming that the proposed pharmacy law was not for the protection of people, as members of the association claimed, but for the protection of a few pharmacists. The members of the association were accused of trying to eliminate competition in a saturated profession. One retail pharmacist claimed that "the matters are actuated by solely selfish motives that should bring the blush of shame to their cheeks, for the object is to lessen competition in pharmacy as a business, instead of elevating the standard education."[5]

The criticism that the IPhA's pharmacy bill was a tool for a few officious egocentrics to protect themselves from unwanted competition was a common accusation throughout the process of procuring the law. Detzer in his 1886 presidential address commented on the criticisms by stating that "some of our fellows are proud to christen those who are actively engaged in our State Associations as cranks. Would there were more of them. History has been made by so-called cranks."[6] Detzer's message was clear. Criticisms would not fall on deaf ears and, as demonstrated by Eliel's evening meeting, would be used to assess the existing language of the proposed law. Furthermore, criticism within the profession would not deter the IPhA from pursuing a cause it deemed noble and for the betterment of Indiana.

Prior to the meeting of the 1887 Legislature, a petition was circulated and signed by several hundred pharmacists announcing their disapproval of the proposed pharmacy law. The petition stated that the law was unequal and oppressive class legislation, it did not secure the citizens of Indiana from danger, it would deprive many areas in Indiana from having a drug store, and that a Board of Pharmacy would create a direct tax of $20,000 dollars annually for pharmacists in Indiana.[7] Although it passed the Senate by a large majority, the proposed pharmacy law was defeated in the House of Representatives. In a fiery letter written to *The Indiana Pharmacist* in April of 1887, then president Leo Eliel berated those who opposed the proposed law for not making their criticisms known publicly at the annual meeting of the association. Eliel stated that if the men had qualms with the legislation they should have met with the Legislative Committee and if "they could not have agreed, opposition would not have the taint of self-interest attached to it, nor would it have been quite so cowardly a proceeding."[8] Eliel blamed the wholesale distributors or jobbers in Indianapolis for the defeat and accused the Indianapolis jobbers of joining the organization for the exclusive purpose of thwarting the proposed pharmacy legislation. Coincidently, the membership of the association increased from 307 members in 1946 to 356 members in 1947.[9]

Eliel's reaction to yet another defeat for the pharmacy bill did not end just with an impassioned letter to *The Indiana Pharmacist*. At the annual meeting of 1887, he called on Indianapolis wholesaler, Mr. Dan Daugherty of the Richardson Drug Co., to explain his opposition to the proposed pharmacy law.[10] Daugherty told the association that he personally was in favor of a pharmacy law for Indiana, however, letters and requests from friends and customers influenced him to lobby against the law. He also mentioned that the Richardson Drug Co. had fought for pharmacy legislation in both Missouri and Nebraska because their customers favored having a law. The wholesalers' opposition was for no other reason than customer demand. If the majority of retail pharmacists wanted the legislation, their desire would have garnered support from the wholesaler. Daugherty shared that some of the Indianapolis wholesalers printed petitions with false claims about scope of the bill and employed lawyers to lobby for its defeat.

Eliel expressed his gratitude to Mr. Daugherty and assurance that he felt no animosity towards any wholesaler about the matter. The two months between Eliel's letter and the annual meeting certainly quelled the disdain he had felt for the Indianapolis jobbers and allowed him to use his time with Mr. Daugherty productively to better understand the criticisms of the pharmacy bill and the motivation behind its defeat.

At the same 1887 meeting, Josiah K. Lilly made a powerful statement regarding the Lilly family's view of the pharmacy bill. "Our house favors the law; always has thrown its influence in favor of every improvement in pharmacy; would be glad to know that we had a law now."[11] The Lilly family had been at the forefront of pharmaceutical research and growth for over a decade in Indianapolis and their influence carried great weight in the association. While the scope of the organization was defined as catering to all the pharmacists in Indianapolis, the association dealt predominantly with issues involving the retail pharmacist. The fact that Colonel Eli Lilly was viewed as a leader during the founding meeting and his son Josiah rarely missed an annual meeting, demonstrates the Lilly family's support of the IPhA. One could say that the Lillys attended the meetings simply to facilitate robust business relationships with many of the pharmacists in the State. This would be a gross understatement of the Lillys involvement within the association. Not only did Josiah Lilly attend nearly every annual meeting, but he also held offices and positions on many committees. The Lillys funded reception dinners for the organization during times of economic hardship, and planned tours of their facilities when the annual meetings were held in Indianapolis. The most beneficial contributions the Lilly's made during the early years of the association were the scientific papers and displays that were present at many of the annual meetings. Josiah used the resources of the Eli Lilly Company to advance the profession in Indiana by sharing with his fellow pharmacists the most recent advancements in pharmaceutical science. There is little evidence of disagreements between the Lillys and the IPhA. Most of Lillys actions were taken as measures to better the profession of pharmacy in Indiana.

With another defeat in the Legislature in 1889, attitudes about the pharmacy bill began to change within the organization. During his presidential address in 1889, Arthur Green proposed that the organization concentrate its efforts on other areas within the State. The association was extremely proud of the Purdue School of Pharmacy; Green opined that if the IPhA had invested as much time, energy, and labor into bettering the pharmacy school as it did into drafting the pharmacy bill, the current state of the profession would consequently increase due to better trained professionals. Many within the organization agreed with Green, and thought that working to achieve higher standards of education should be a higher priority than procuring pharmacy legislation.

In the meantime, both Detzer and Eliel, the champions of pharmacy legislation for the previous seven years, changed their opinions about a Hoosier pharmacy law. In a paper read to the association about the failures during the 1889 Legislature, Eliel concluded by stating, "Individually, I shall henceforth be found in the ranks of those opposing legislation so far as Indiana is concerned."[12] After four defeats in the Legislature and seven years of onerous labor, it is understandable that both Detzer and Eliel were frustrated with the entire process. John Hurty, who had also devoted time to the bill himself, recognized their change of heart as just that, a frustrated vacillation due to their fervent efforts.

> Now, Mr. Eliel finds himself opposed to any kind of pharmacy bill, and Mr. Detzer, too. I am sorry to see that. Those gentlemen are enthusiasts, we know that. I thank God they are enthusiasts, and if they were not we would not have such good pharmaceutical work out of them. They have worked at it out of pure enthusiasm. But that same enthusiasm has made their pendulum swing clear to the other side. But I know they do not intend it. They are in for progress, and we are all in for progress.[13]

Furthermore, Hurty proposed a resolution to change the appointments to the Legislative Committee so to include five retail pharmacists and at least two wholesalers. Before the motion was accepted Eliel asserted that the committee should have "fresh blood", consisting of members who have never contributed to the Legislative Committee.[14] The motion passed, and with Detzer and Eliel's departure, the task of procuring the pharmacy bill lost two of its most ardent champions.

The pharmacy bill met with two more defeats in the Legislature in 1891 and 1893. What started as one of the primary endeavors for the IPhA now became a matter of ambivalence and at times, pride in the fact that Indiana was not tethered to a stringent pharmacy law. John Hurty, who in 1889 proposed a new Legislative Committee, softened his stance in his presidential year of 1891 by stating that the entire State may not be ready for a comprehensive pharmacy law and that drafting a bill that governed over only the larger cities may be a more prudent course of action. By 1893 Hurty, who was part of the Legislative Committee that year, had joined Eliel and Detzer in thinking that a pharmacy law may not be in the best interest of either IPhA or Indiana.

The IPhA and the Purdue School of Pharmacy often received inquiries asking about the pharmacy laws in Indiana and requirements for licensure. Whether out of genuine pride or exacerbated frustration, Hurty responded to one such inquiry about licensed pharmacists and drug stores in Indiana by stating that, "The druggists of Indiana don't need to be protected, and her citizens have wit enough to avoid poor, unworthy druggists. Any person can open a store in this commonwealth, but only the fit survive. I hope that we will never see the day when the pharmacists will be so weak as to need the protection of law, or when our people will be such idiots that they can't tell a good druggist from a poor one."[15] Hurty's response was typical of many members of the IPhA who had become disenchanted with the pharmacy bill.

The bills proposed from 1894 to 1898 were plagued by the same problems as in previous years. Above all, the jobbers maintained that their customers did not want legislation. There were also now mixed feelings in the IPhA about the utility of a pharmacy law, and previous staunch supporters of the bill focused their efforts on improving the Purdue School of Pharmacy or serving as delegates to national organizations. Even though the pharmacy bill was devoid of Eliel, Detzer, and Hurty's efforts, other enthusiastic supporters breathed new life into a tired cause. In 1898, the Legislative Committee came closer than any other committee in the previous decade to attaining a pharmacy law. In fact, the bill passed both Houses, but the Governor failed to sign it into law.

Learning from the mistakes of the previous year, Legislative Committee chairman R. I. Eads and committee members F.E. Wolcott and R.P. Blodau decided to seek the Governor's approval before proposing a bill to the Legislature. On December 5, 1898, the Legislative Committee met with the Governor to share the differences and similarities of the new bill to the one that he had not signed the previous year. After hearing the suggestions of the Governor, the committee revised the bill and with support from the Governor, mailed each Legislator a copy of the revised bill on January 9, 1899. The challenge in previous years had been that the bill stalled in the House of Representatives, inundated by unfavorable amendments and victim to inimical review committees. However, in 1899 the amendments proposed by the House were carefully managed by the Legislative Committee and with the aid of a helpful House Committee, the bill passed on February 3, 1899.

On February 9 during the eighteenth annual meeting of the IPhA, R. I. Eads reported on the tenuous situation involving House Bill No. 47. For fear that the bill would be buried, the Legislative Committee accepted the proposed amendments from the House and submitted the bill to the historically more sympathetic Senate. Eads advised the association to meet with their Senator to discuss Bill 47 and stress the importance of accepting it as written. He warned that if the bill was altered at all it must return to the House for concurrence and chances of passage would be much diminished.

The efforts of Eads and the others came to fruition shortly after the annual meeting of 1899. House Bill No. 47was passed by the Senate and signed by the Governor, and thus became Indiana's first Pharmacy Practice Act. Hoosier pharmacists had finally gained the protection they had sought since the founding of the organization. As it turned out, Indiana became the last State in the Union to pass a pharmacy law. Nonetheless, Eads and the others succeeded where many others had failed, and they held fast to the idea of protecting the profession of pharmacy in Indiana when others had given up hope.

With the enactment of the Practice Act, Indiana established the State Board of Pharmacy and with that, the IPhA started its close working relationship with the Board. The Board would be in charge of registering pharmacists and assistant pharmacists and issuing licenses for practice. Pharmacists who had owned their own stores prior to the passage of the bill needed to simply apply for a license. Pharmacists who did not own their own

The First Indiana Board of Pharmacy (1899). Top Row - Harry E. Glick, Lafayette; George W. Sloan, Indianapolis. Second Row - Charles Crecelius, New Albany, Secretary; Theodore F. Otto, Columbus; Charles P. Woodworth, Fort Wayne, President.

store needed to work as a clerk for four years and pass an examination administered by the Board. To become a registered assistant pharmacist, an individual either had to have worked for two years as a clerk at a pharmacy during the time of passage or work for two years as a clerk and pass the Board examination. Graduates from approved schools of pharmacy could substitute the years attended for years of service when applying for a license. Anyone found not abiding by the law would be charged with a misdemeanor and be subject to a penalty of no more than one-hundred dollars and no less than five dollars. The enactment of Indiana's pharmacy law was an important step in securing the professional status of Hoosier pharmacists and ensuring that individuals not licensed by other States did not seek refuge in the now tamed, Wild West of Pharmacy.

Pioneers of Education

The organization of the Indiana State Board of Pharmacy introduced a new culture within the profession with added emphasis on the skill and especially the knowledge of the pharmacist. In no other facet of the profession were the members of the IPhA more proud than with their association with the Purdue University School of Pharmacy. The IPhA's own John Hurty is often

Bruno Knoefel—first pharmacist license issued in Indiana.

given credit with founding the school. This is true, but the catalyst for the school's founding was a rather unremarkable conversation in 1883 between Hurty and James H. Smart, the fourth president of Purdue University. It took place in Hurty's Indianapolis drugstore during an informal gathering of some of the local professionals whereby Hurty and Smart came to mutual agreement that Smart would propose a school of pharmacy at the next Board meeting if Hurty would agree to a two year professorship at the university.[16] One year later in the fall of 1884, the Purdue School of Pharmacy opened its doors to seven students seeking their Graduate in Pharmacy (PhG) degrees.

The IPhA and the Purdue School of Pharmacy had a very close, mutually beneficial relationship during the early years of both institutions. The relationship began with the formation of the IPhA's Committee on Education. The duties of the committee were to report on the current curriculum implemented by the faculty, the number and quality of students, and implementing a practical examination. A typical practical examination in the early years of the relationship consisted of the identification of at least fifteen pharmacopeial drugs and preparations. These samples were often furnished from Eli Lilly & Co. in Indianapolis and students had the opportunity to either identify the substances using senses or by chemical analysis. A score of seventy percent was considered acceptable on the identification portion of the examination and students were also subjected to oral questions and a prescription examination.[17]

As the relationship between the Purdue School of Pharmacy and the IPhA developed, additional theoretical exams were administered to the students by the Committee on Education. These consisted of at least ten questions in Pharmacy, Chemistry, and Materia Medica. The IPhA was progressive and a national leader in its educational initiatives. At the annual meeting of 1891, President John Hurty shared with his fellow members that the American Pharmaceutical Association (APhA) recommended additional exams administered by state associations to supplement those of the faculty. Hurty informed the APhA that this idea was not innovative and that the IPhA had been administering such exams shortly after the founding of the State's first pharmacy school. In typical Hurty fashion, he boasted to the IPhA that, "I told them they were just catching up."[18] Massachusetts was one of the only other States to administer supplemental examinations, and it had adopted the educational methods of the IPhA. The IPhA stood alone among state associations as an outside organization having the authority to administer examinations and approve or disapprove potential graduates.

Leo Eliel served many terms on the Committee on Education and was also a professor at Purdue University School of Pharmacy during his time with the IPhA. Eliel applauded the graduates of Purdue with the utmost enthusiasm but at the same time never remained complacent. He consistently urged the association to work with Purdue to increase the educational standards for acceptance and graduation from the program. He was also adamant about implementing a two year apprenticeship as part of the matriculation requirements. While the IPhA was in agreement that practical experience was a necessary part of pharmacy education, there was disagreement about whether the apprenticeship should come before, during, or after pharmacy school. The IPhA adopted resolutions during the 1902 annual meeting employing the Legislative Committee to amend the pharmacy law to include matters of apprenticeship and education. Specifically, in regards to age and educational requirements and when the apprenticeship should take place.

By 1908 Indiana had six schools of pharmacy, Purdue University School of Pharmacy, Lafayette; Tri-State College of Pharmacy, Angola; Northern Indiana School of Pharmacy, Valparaiso; University of Notre Dame, Department of Pharmacy, South Bend; Winona School of Pharmacy, Indianapolis; and St. Mary's Academy, South Bend. Whether out of limited time and man-power to administer examinations to potential graduates of all the institutions or because of more comprehensive examinations by the individual institutions, the IPhA's supplemental examinations were discontinued. The IPhA did maintain its strong relationship with Purdue and continued to send the Committee on Education to assess the state of pharmacy education in Indiana. The 1908 committee reported that some of the work done by the IPhA to increase admittance and graduation requirements as well as improving educational standards had come to fruition. The length of the program had increased to two full years with nine months of course work per year. The degree had changed at Purdue from Ph. G. to a Ph. C. or pharmaceutical chemist. Purdue required each entrant to have at least one year of high school course work prior to admittance. Following the first three months of course work, the faculty had prepared the students to pass the State Board's examination for assistant pharmacists. Most notably, Purdue had implemented a one-year post-graduate course in analytical chemistry and bacteriology.

The IPhA's enthusiasm towards education during the progressive era was a mutually beneficial endeavor. The schools of pharmacy, especially at Purdue, benefited from the leadership and guidance of some of the most eminent pharmacists in the State. In turn, the IPhA was able to have an active role in improving the status of the profession by participating in the education of young, well trained, and intelligent students. As the educational standards of the schools rose, so too did the expectations of the IPhA. The constant attention to education secured Indiana's position as a national leader in the area of pharmacy education. During times of frustration and disappointment with the struggle to enact a pharmacy law, Hoosier pharmacists were able to take pride in their efforts to improve the quality of education in the State.

A Web of Business Plagues: Patent Medicines, "Cut-rating", and Physician Competition

The progress of the IPhA in the areas of legislation and education helped to bolster the professional status of pharmacy in Indiana. During the course of these efforts, Hoosier pharmacists were faced with many obstacles that proved to be deleterious to their pocket books. The IPhA sought to maintain a balance between their duties to professionalism and their duties to improve the economics of their business. The three connected issues of patent medicines, "cut-rating", and physician competition were detrimental to the business of pharmacy in Indiana. During this era in pharmacy, your enemies and allies changed quickly and often and many times, progress to resolve one problem would lead to the creation of a new one. While these three problems affected all facets of Hoosier pharmacy in some way, the retail pharmacists were not constantly in battle throughout the progressive era. Given that the IPhA was primarily comprised of retail pharmacists, these challenges resulted in a strong bond with the National Association of Retail Druggists (NARD) and relied on their help to facilitate change on a national level.

During the twelve years of economic hardship for Hoosier pharmacists blame was ascribed to the manufacturers and wholesalers of patent medicines. The idea that eliminating the sale of patent remedies would cease the practice of cutting prices was persistent in the IPhA. This notion was maintained for the better part of the depression. During the annual meeting of 1891, Leo Eliel introduced the Tripartite Plan that he had learned about at a meeting of the Association of Manufacturers and Dealers in Proprietary Articles (AMDPA) held the month prior in New York City. The plan was a collaborative effort by the AMDPA and the APhA that called for the manufacturer's support of any plan of the APhA to prevent the cutting of prices in retail stores. Furthermore, the plan stated that manufacturers should abstain from selling goods to any entity that violates the agreement and that the APhA wanted each state association to endorse the plan within their own State. The plan was passed by the AMDPA and the APhA proceeded to formulate the following plan:

First – Manufacturers and owners of proprietary medicines on the contract plan agree to sell their products to druggists only.

Second – Wholesale druggists or distributing agents agree to sell contract goods solely to druggists, excepting in those localities where no druggists are in business. Wholesale druggists are not to supply any dealer on the cut-off list. Further, wholesale druggists agree not to substitute when any order is presented for any article on the contract plan.

Third – Retail druggists to sign an agreement, including all contracts or rebate articles, that they will not violate the conditions of said agreement, and further agree not to substitute another article for any article required that is on the contract or rebate plan, nor deliver such goods to any dealer on the cut-off list. And it is hereby provided that the names of all druggists who fail to sign the agreement be placed on the cut-off list.

Fourth – Under no consideration shall any manufacturer, wholesale or retail druggist, directly or by collusion, supply any proprietary preparation on the contract plan to dealers on the cut-off list.

Fifth – Manufacturers and wholesale and retail druggists shall refuse to sell commission merchants, brokers, expressmen or agents any article on the contract plan, unless such sales are for export or for purchasers who are removed from domestic competition.

Sixth – Manufacturers and wholesale druggists or distributors of articles on the contract plan to agree not to sell such articles to any retailer of said articles who will not agree to sell at full retail price.

Seventh – Manufacturers of proprietary articles on the contract plan to make their contracts in such a manner as not to materially increase the purchasing price of the retailer.

Eighth – Any wholesale or retail druggist violating his contract shall be placed on the cut-off list as a penalty of such a violation.[19]

The decision before the IPhA was whether or not to endorse the plan as proposed at the national level. There were mixed feelings about the Tripartite Plan, those in favor saw the opportunity to eliminate price cutting for good and those opposed saw the plan as a way for the manufacturers of patent medicines to avoid a comprehensive boycott of their goods by respectable retailers. Another concern about the proposed plan was with substituting one's own preparation for a patent. After much debate the members of the IPhA concluded that the ethics that had always governed their actions in this situation was still applicable under this plan. If a patron asked for a product by a brand name it was their duty to vend the desired product. If a patron asked for a remedy by a generic name, the pharmacist could sell their own mixture. Josiah Lilly as a manufacturer of non-secret medicines endorsed this action from the perspective of a neutral party. Following a lengthy debate about the pros and cons of the plan, the IPhA decided to endorse the plan and abide by the conditions set forth by the APhA.

The proposal of the Tripartite Plan was important for several reasons. First, it was a catalyst for the unification of the manufacturers, wholesalers, and retailers against cutting prices. Second, it engendered a shift in attitude from blaming price cutting on patent medicines to blaming the problem on the "cut-rating" retailers themselves. In the years to come, this attitude would persist and patent medicines would no longer be the enemy of the retailer, but a valued medicinal option.

In November of 1891, the Tripartite Committee was formed from representatives of the manufacturer, wholesale, and retail pharmacists to finalize the Tripartite Plan. However, members of the manufacturers were afraid of violating anti-trust laws that were implemented during the progressive era. By April of 1892 the Tripartite Plan "died of fright", when, after consulting their lawyers, the manufacturers decided not to sign the agreement.[20] All was not lost. During the summer of 1891, a meeting of retailers and wholesalers in St. Louis, Missouri was called to implement a similar agreement to that of the Tripartite Plan. Following a marked improvement in business, a larger meeting was called to form an interstate association from the towns and cities located in the Mississippi valley. From the meeting, the Interstate Retail Druggists League was born, relying on the cooperation of the wholesale and retail pharmacists. The League carefully proposed a plan similar to the Tripartite Plan but assured that the plan was not in violation of the anti-trust laws. The plan was similar in spirit to that of the Tripartite Plan and placed pressure on the manufacturers by agreeing not to purchase products from those that sold to wholesalers or retailers that cut prices. The IPhA was well represented at this first meeting, sending George W. Sloan, Frank H. Carter, and H.E. Zimmer to handle the affairs of Indiana. The IPhA fully endorsed the plan of the Inter-State Retail Druggists League and maintained presence within the organization.

In subsequent years, the NARD carried the torch of the Inter-State Retail Druggists League and improved on the previous plan. In addition to collaborating with the wholesalers, the NARD proposed the Serial Numbering Plan with the manufacturers. By individually marking products, the NARD was able to trace goods sold from wholesalers to cutters. The new plan placed the responsibility on all three facets of the pharmaceutical business and was successful throughout the nation. The IPhA had a strong relationship with the NARD and pursued implementation of the plans in Indiana. The IPhA adopted both the Direct Contract Plan and the Serial Numbering Plan forming alliances with reputable manufacturers and wholesalers in the State and across the Nation. Representatives from the NARD were frequent guests at the IPhA annual meetings and often aided with legislative affairs and other matters in Indiana. In turn the IPhA promoted the NARD within the organization and established a committee to attend their meetings and carry the NARD agenda within the duties of the association.

The Direct Contract Plan and the Serial Numbering Plan reshaped the old paradigm concerning patent medicine. Retail pharmacists were making money from its sale and patents became an integral part of the Hoosier drugstore. During the 1905 General Assembly of Indiana, a formula bill was proposed to list the ingredients of all secret patents. Manufacturers stressed that if the bill passed they would cease selling patents in Indiana. The IPhA deemed the sale of patent medicines important enough to lend their full support in opposing the passage of the bill.

We know now that many of the patent medicines sold during the progressive era contained opiates, high volumes of alcohol, and other habit forming substances that were detrimental to the health of society. Many attribute the end of patent medicines and the "cut-rate" problem to the muckraking reporting of Samuel Hopkins Adams and his piece "The Great American Fraud" that was published in Collier's, *The National Weekly*. His piece was one of the catalysts for the passage of the national 1906 Pure Food and Drug Act.[21] Much like the progressive efforts of the IPhA with pharmaceutical education, Indiana was at the forefront of pure food and drug legislation. John Hurty was elected secretary of the IPhA and State Health Commissioner in 1896; in 1897 he and others proposed a first draft of a Pure Food and Drug bill to the General Assembly. Two years later the 1899 Legislature passed Indiana's Pure Food and Drug Law. Hurty's close work with the IPhA and his experience as a retail pharmacist undoubtedly influenced his aggressive pursuit to obtain the legislation. Even with the law on the books, the practical enforcement of the law was not possible until the 1905 legislation funding the Indiana State Board of Health's Laboratory of Hygiene. The Laboratory of Hygiene employed a State Chemist with the duties of testing food and drugs to ensure their safety. The passage of the 1906 National Food and Drug Act only strengthened the power of the state legislation. With

Hurty's leadership, the Laboratory of Hygiene became an effective tool for securing the safety of all Hoosiers.

The IPhA fully endorsed the Pure Food and Drug Act and asserted that only those drugs that were contained in the United States Pharmacopoeia and the National Formulary were to be sold in Indiana drugstores. The safety and well-being of the citizens of Indiana had a primary importance over the profits that could be made from the sale of dangerous patents.

With the aid and guidance of the NARD and the diligent efforts of the State Laboratory of Hygiene, the IPhA saw a great reduction in the practices of cutting prices and the sale of dangerous patent medicines. The active endorsement of the IPhA of the Harrison Narcotic Act in 1915 reduced the practice of selling immoderate amounts of habit-forming narcotics that could potentially addict patrons. The safety and well-being of Indiana citizens was placed at the forefront of IPhA duties and in turn the profession of pharmacy was elevated in the eyes of the public and business was better because of their actions.

One limitation of the Pure Food and Drug Act was the inability of the State Laboratory of Hygiene to test the drugs sold to physicians. Under the law physicians were exempt from such testing and could dispense drugs to their patients without undergoing the same process as the pharmacist. The IPhA did not disagree with the principle of the Pure Food and Drug Act; on the contrary, they supported it wholeheartedly. They simply wanted the Act to be comprehensive and place pharmacists and physicians on equal footing. The IPhA viewed the unequal enactment of the law as unfair practice and claimed that it allowed for the physician to purchase a subpar quality of drugs and to substitute in times when the desired drug was not available. Hoosier pharmacists often debated the role of the physician to the pharmacist and the similarity in codes of ethics that bind the two professions. During the 1911 annual meeting, many members proposed that the Legislative Committee pursue a law to prohibit the dispensing of drugs by physicians. The pursuit of such legislation proved fruitless, and the precarious connection with the physician continued through the end of the progressive era. The professional prominence that Hoosier pharmacists gained during the progressive era did not go in vain. Many pharmacists sought out the more reputable physicians and made working agreements to utilize the expertise of the pharmacist to fill prescriptions. Many physicians made such agreements and a trend to utilize the pharmacist in a greater capacity was established.

Conclusion

Hoosier pharmacy during the progressive era was an often tumultuous but very productive period in the development of the profession. The efforts of progressives such as Eliel and Hurty shaped the agenda of the IPhA during this period of transformation. Like many progressive organizations, the IPhA sought to improve the condition of Indiana citizens. Even though the first *Monthly Bulletin of the Indiana State Board of Health* was published in 1899, the monthly publication of the IPhA, *The Indiana Pharmacist*, acted as a source for public health information for the previous two decades. *The Indiana Pharmacist* contained numerous articles about the danger of smoking and alcohol use and maxims about proper nutrition, recommended sleep, and how to live longer. The IPhA was serving the cause of public health not just through properly dispensing medicine, but in all facets of life. The public health articles in *The Indiana Pharmacist* illustrate the strong connection that the IPhA had with the health of Hoosiers.

In addition to tending to the public health of Indiana, the IPhA made great gains in securing both professional prominence and economic security. The relentless efforts of the Legislative Committee procured the first Pharmacy Practice Act to safeguard the profession from unqualified pharmacists and establish a State Board of Pharmacy. By implementing supplemental testing, the Committee on Education helped to elevate the Purdue School of Pharmacy to one of the premier schools in the nation. The active involvement of the IPhA with the NARD met the problem of "cut-rating" head-on to bolster the economic security of Indiana pharmacists.

Section 2 Endnotes

1 "President's Address", *Indiana Pharmacist*, 5 no. 2 (1886): 41.

2 Ibid., 39.

3 Lewis L. Gould, *America in the Progressive Era: 1890-1914* (New York: Longman, 2001), 21.

4 *Proceedings of the Indiana Pharmaceutical Association for the Years 1886 to 1889* (Indianapolis: Journal Job Printing Company, 1889), 27.

5 "Benefits (?) of Pharmacy Laws", *The Indiana Pharmacist*, 5 no. 4 (1886), 107.

6 *Proceedings of the Indiana Pharmaceutical Association for the Years 1886 to 1889*, 14.

7 "That Petition", *The Indiana Pharmacist*, 5 no. 12 (1887), 357.

8 Leo Eliel, "The Pharmacy Law", *The Indiana Pharmacist*, 5 no. 12 (1887), 358.

9 *Proceedings of the Indiana Pharmaceutical Association for th Years 1886 to 1889*, 68.

10 Ibid., 79.

11 Ibid., 80.

12 Ibid., 201.

13 Ibid., 210-211.

14 Ibid., 215.

15 "Pharmacy Law in Indiana", *The Indiana Pharmacist*, 12 no. 8 (1893): 250.

16 Robert B. Eckles, *Purdue Pharmacy: The First Century* (West Lafayette: Purdue Research Foundation, 1979), 1.

17 *Proceedings of the Indiana Pharmaceutical Association for the years 1886 -1889*, 22.

18 *Proceedings of the Tenth Annual Meeting of the Indiana Pharmaceutical Association* (LaPorte, Indiana: Wadsworth & Kessler, Printers, 1892), 62.

19 Ibid., 14.

20 *Proceedings of the Eleventh Annual Meeting of the Indiana Pharmaceutical Association* (Laporte, Indiana: Wadsworth & Kessler, Printers, 1892), 11.

21 James Harvey Young, *The Toadstool Millionaires: A Social History of Patent Medicines before Federal Regulation*

LICENSED PHARMACY
TO COMPOUND PRESCRIPTIONS
AND SELL DRUGS

TO SAFEGUARD HEALTH

Member

INDIANA
PHARMACEUTICAL
ASSOCIATION
1918-1940

*Consolidating
Advance in
Professional
Pharmacy
between
the Wars*

The tumultuous decades following the progressive era were a time of consolidation for the IPhA. In addition, new opportunities opened, for example, as a result of federal and State prohibition laws that gave pharmacists responsibility to legally dispense alcohol for medicinal purposes. The IPhA lobbied for legislation to safeguard the profession from bootleggers and all others that would discredit Hoosier pharmacy with illegal practices.

When prohibition ended in 1933, the Nation was in the midst of widespread economic hardships associated with the Great Depression. Because chain drugstores were increasing in numbers during this time, the ability of the stores to carry high volume and sell at low prices caused an economic pinch for the independent retail pharmacist. The IPhA was a fervent supporter of Fair Trade Laws and lobbied within the State to procure Fair Trade Legislation in Indiana prior to the passage of the Federal Tydings Miller Bill. The association asserted that Fair Trade Laws were a "square deal" for all pharmacists and informed Hoosiers that the laws were not intended to fix prices but increase fair competition.

The IPhA established a full-time headquarters in 1927 located in New Albany, Indiana and later relocated to its current home in Indianapolis in 1938. The establishment of a permanent full-time headquarters provided better accommodations to facilitate the business of the organization. It also acted as a symbol to Hoosier pharmacists of the permanence and commitment of the organization. The IPhA further demonstrated its commitment to Hoosier pharmacists in 1937 after a flood of the Ohio River Valley that devastated the supplies, equipment, and buildings of many pharmacies in southern Indiana. The IPhA solicited all pharmacists in the State to donate money to the flood relief fund and inquired with manufacturers about replacing lost or damaged supplies to their customers.

Exclusivity and Permanence during Prohibition

Indiana voted a state-wide prohibition law in 1917 which became law on April 2, 1918.[1] Two years after Indiana's "bone dry" law was enacted, Federal prohibition was enacted on January 16, 1920 by way of the Eighteenth Amendment and the Volstead Act. Under State and Federal prohibition, every pharmacist in Indiana who carried alcohol had to purchase three separate bonds in order to legally stock, purchase, and dispense the prohibited item. One bond was given to the Federal Collector to obtain the non-beverage permit and the other two bonds were given to the county clerk in exchange for permits to sell and receive alcohol. Legally, pharmacists were only allowed to either sell alcohol for medical purposes in accordance with the ten government formulae, or wine to church officials for use as a sacrament.

Some of the problems associated with these responsibilities are described by Pete Honorof, member of the IPhA, who lamented in a letter to the *Indiana Pharmacist* about the state of pharmacy before the Indiana and the federal prohibition acts, "The prohibition movement from its infancy, beginning with the Local Option Period has turned pharmacy into a dumping ground for booze – refugee and asylum for Barkeepers and Bootleggers."[2] Prior to Indiana's prohibition act of 1917, the State implemented a Local Option plan allowing individual counties to prohibit the sale of liqueur within its own borders. Dry county saloons maintained business by continuing alcohol sales under the guise of being a drugstore. Reputable pharmacists scoffed at the transformation, expressing their amusement with the saying, "Hush little bar room, don't you cry, you will be a drug store by and by."[3] Unfortunately for the Hoosier pharmacists living in dry counties, many of the transformed saloons evolved into chain cut-rate drugstores through collaboration of the former saloon owners. Reputable pharmacists who previously mocked the former saloons resorted to selling alcohol in an effort to remain competitive.

The IPhA viewed the passage of Indiana's prohibition bill as a much needed blessing. The "bone dry" law aided in eliminating competition from the former saloons and restored some of the professional prominence that was lost during the Local Option period. Honorof sympathized with his fellow pharmacists by concluding his letter stating, "He is a pharmacist. Pharmacy is his profession, his thought and his ambition and it was the miserable competition of the Local Option period that forced him to engage in the filthy blind pig business."[4]

Similar to the Harrison Narcotic Act before it, prohibition laws bestowed an element of exclusivity to the pharmacist. The IPhA consistently advocated the benefits of regulation, citing the Narcotic Act and the "bone dry" law as examples of legislation placing a greater responsibility and importance on the pharmacist. During the early years of prohibition, the Legislative Committee of the IPhA understood the importance of regulation for professional development and fought hard to ensure that regulation not only worked, but worked for Hoosier pharmacists. In 1921, the Legislative Committee proposed an amendment to Indiana's prohibition law to better harmonize it with the Volstead act. The amendment restricted the sale of alcohol to only those individuals who obtained a permit from the State Board of Pharmacy. The amendment allowed for better enforcement of the prohibition law and eliminated competition from unregistered merchants selling alcohol remedies. In 1921, the Legislature also lobbied for an amendment to the prohibition law that allowed pharmacists to obtain the Federal alcohol permit in place of the state permits. The amendment saved Hoosier pharmacists $13.50 annually. The IPhA's efforts to lobby for these two amendments during the infancy of prohibition made supporting regulation easier for Hoosier pharmacists.

Federal legislation limited the power of state and local governments to amend its prohibition laws to any great extent. For the most part, the IPhA was content with the existing law and welcomed the new exclusivity pharmacists incurred from its enactment. The IPhA's Legislative Committee focused its efforts on thwarting bills that would be detrimental to pharmacy as a profession and as a business. Soda fountains, candy displays, ice cream, advertisements, and eye-catching window displays were a welcome addition to drugstores in the early twenties. Hoosier pharmacists also became accustomed to new types of legislation that followed from their new business activities. Bills were proposed to tax sales of soda, ice cream, and candy. Grocers and other eateries proposed bills to prohibit drugstores from selling food stuff in areas where other venues were available. Ironically, the Legislative Committee of the IPhA tried to defend its interests by using some of the same lobbying tactics of burdening bills with amendments that was used against them twenty years prior when trying to pass the first Practice Act. Throughout the twenties, the IPhA followed this defensive philosophy, lobbying to preclude the passage of adverse bills rather than proposing and lobbying for new, favorable ones.

An exception to this rule came during the 1923 meeting of the General Assembly, when the Legislative Committee was able to successfully lobby for new legislation beneficial to the profession. The legislative program for 1923 included proposed bills for defining a drugstore, a pharmacy, and a pharmacist; raising the fees to take examinations from the State Board of Pharmacy; amending the State Prerequisite Law; changing the re-registration fee; and implementing a Poison Law. The bills proposing increases in examination and re-registration fees were designed to aid the State Board of Pharmacy financially so it could monitor the profession with greater efficiency with less financial restriction. Furthermore, the increased re-registration fee included dues to become a member of the IPhA, meaning that every registered pharmacist in Indiana would also belong to the State association. The amendment to Indiana's Prerequisite Law was necessary to coincide with federal legislation requiring that all individuals attend four years of high school prior to entering pharmacy school. The proposed Poison Bill was a proactive defensive maneuver, since the legislative committee had been lobbying against poorly written Poison Bills in years prior. The most important of the proposed bills was the one defining a drugstore, pharmacist, and pharmacy. With clearly defined terms the IPhA hoped to distinguish between those qualified to dispense medicines and those that were not.

The 1923 legislative plan of the IPhA was a large success. Two bills passed providing more funds for the State Board of Pharmacy and financial means to enforce the laws that the IPhA had fought for over the years. The bill to raise the re-registration fee of pharmacists not only provided more funds for the State Board but also provided the IPhA with a small part of the fee to promote pharmacy in the State. The bill to define the terms drugstore, pharmacy, and pharmacist, known as Senate Bill 174, passed allowing only individuals licensed as a registered pharmacist by the Indiana Board of Pharmacy or a corporation employing a registered pharmacist to legally use the title drugstore, pharmacy, apothecary, or any similar title for their business. The IPhA viewed this law as "the most progressive step ever taken by this or any other State to give just recognition to the qualified registered pharmacist."[5] This law provided additional exclusivity for the profession and was important in establishing the pharmacy as a trusted and reliable place for the public to purchase their medicinal goods.

State and Federal narcotics and prohibition acts bestowed greater responsibility on the pharmacist as an exclusive dispenser of medicinal items. The IPhA maintained that these greater responsibilities required all Hoosier pharmacists to strive for a higher standard of professional practice. In April of 1922 *The Indiana Pharmacist* published a moral code for pharmacists entitled "Principles of Pharmaceutical Ethics". The principles included ethical conduct when dealing with the public, the relationship to the physician, and duties to other pharmacists and the profession. By publicizing the principles in *The Indiana Pharmacist*, the IPhA exhibited its commitment to ethical practice and its support of the standards printed.

When dealing with the public, the principles state that first and foremost the pharmacist was morally obligated to ensure the safety of any patron, be a lawful citizen, and be an advocate for public health. To properly adhere to these moral dictums, it was the pharmacists' responsibility to seek adequate training to meet the qualifications of the state. The pharmacist should only prepare remedies approved by the United States Pharmacopeia and the National Formulary and avoid substituting ingredients and dispensing products of a poor quality. The principles also stated that it was the duty of the pharmacist to maintain a clean and sanitary store, safeguard patrons from habit forming-drugs, maintain the confidentiality of a patron's malady, and gain the confidence of the community.[6]

"Principles of Pharmaceutical Ethics" clearly identified the relationship of the pharmacist to the physician. Under no circumstance was the pharmacist justified in diagnosing the illness of a patron or dispensing medicine without a prescription from a physician. The pharmacist must explicitly follow the directions of the physician's prescription and if there was any concern with the prescription, the pharmacist and the physician should meet confidentially to resolve the issue. Furthermore, the pharmacist was not obligated to discuss the therapeutic effects of a remedy or disclose the details of a prescription's composition that were not already given by the physician.[7] If a patron inquired about the therapeutic effects of composition, it was the pharmacist's duty to refer the patron back to the physician for more details.

Many of the principles guiding the obligations of the pharmacist to the profession had been stressed by the IPhA since the organization's inception: Duties such as advancing professional knowledge, participation in pharmaceutical organizations, and exposing dishonesty and corruption in the profession. The principles also stated obligations of professional courtesies such as lending advice or supplies to fellow pharmacists, not copying the labels of competitors, and not filling orders brought in error. Business matters were also addressed insofar as the pharmacist was obligated to report excess or undercharged goods to wholesalers and manufacturers and to adhere to trade regulations and contractual agreements.

The maxims stated in the "Principles of Pharmaceutical Ethics" had been tacitly understood by members of the organization for years. However, in printing the code of ethics, the IPhA served two distinct purposes. It presented a set of standards supported by the association as a unified document, and by publishing the principles in *The Indiana Pharmacist*, the IPhA was able to distribute the standards to all of its members. With the profession of pharmacy growing and becoming more regulated from the 1920's through the 1940's, it was important to establish a code of ethics that the association could stand behind and expand as it grew with the profession.

In addition to the exclusivity and responsibility pharmacists incurred during the prohibition era, they also achieved a sense of permanence with their State association. At the annual meeting of 1927, the IPhA passed a resolution to establish a permanent headquarters for the association. One year prior, Earl Goodnight first proposed the matter in his presidential address to the association. While the resolution was voted down in 1926, Goodnight maintained his support in 1927 and with his guidance and wisdom, the resolution was adopted by the association. Frank V. McCullough from New Albany, Indiana was the acting secretary and editor of *The Indiana Pharmacist* when the resolution passed. The importance of the official "organ" of the association and the necessity for the secretary to have a suitable place to receive correspondence and edit *The Indiana Pharmacist* undoubtedly had a role in establishing the headquarters in New Albany. President Herman Bill and McCullough implemented the resolution, eventually establishing the first permanent home of the IPhA in the Elsby Building in the downtown district of New Albany. The establishment of a headquarters provided McCullough with a suitable place to conduct the business of the association and give *The Indiana Pharmacist* the home that it deserved. More importantly, the new home of the IPhA was a symbol of permanence for the association and its members.

The Rise of Chain Stores and the Struggle for Fair Trade

The reactions against prohibition eventually led to the Cullen-Harrison bill, the 21st Amendment, and the state wide referendum repealing prohibition in Indiana. As prohibition fell out of favor throughout the nation, the country began to slip into a national depression. Like others, Hoosier pharmacists were hit hard by the economic decline that plagued the nation. During the years of 1930 and 1931, *The Indiana Pharmacist* reported a decrease in pharmacy sales of twenty to thirty percent and in some cases, sales plummeted by as much as fifty percent.[8] The plight of the independent retailer was exacerbated by the advent of the chain drugstore and its ability to reduce prices to sell a higher volume of product.

Nationally, from January 1, 1917, to January 21, 1921, ten large chain store systems grew from a total of 496 stores to 1,267.[9] By 1932, the number of chain store systems had grown to 249 with 3,513 stores and sales of approximately $312,000,000 annually.[10] The ability of the chain stores to buy high volumes of merchandise and sell at prices below the independent retailer was a primary concern for the IPhA for nearly two decades. The association maintained as they had in the past that price-cutting was an unfair business practice and that doing so was to the economic detriment of the profession.

In 1925, U.S. Senator Arthur Capper of Kansas and U.S. Representative Clyde Kelly of Pennsylvania proposed a solution for price-cutting in a bill later called the Capper-Kelly Fair Trade Bill. The bill proposed that manufacturers producing goods of the same kind and quality in a fair and competitive market could establish a retail price for their goods. The IPhA stood behind the bill and even appointed a committee to oversee national legislation and assist in any way for the passage of the Capper-Kelly bill. Opponents of Fair Trade laws maintained that any law that fixes prices was in direct violation with the Sherman Anti-Trust Acts. Proponents of the laws including the IPhA asserted that establishing a minimum price for comparable goods increases competition by leveling the playing field.

In 1929, the IPhA legislative committee lobbied for a bill to tax chain stores in Indiana. The Chain Store Tax Law was enacted on July 1st of the same year and provided that each mercantile establishment pay an annual license fee of three dollars when acting as a single unit. Owners operating from two to five stores were responsible for paying ten dollars on each additional store and fifteen dollars for each store from five to ten. The fee was twenty dollars for each store totaling more than ten but less than twenty and twenty five dollars for stores in excess of twenty.[11] Understandably, many of the chain store owners in Indiana were displeased with the law. Lafayette Jackson, owner and operator of 225 grocery and meat stores in Indianapolis, brought suit to test the constitutionality of the law. On February 1, 1930, the Federal District Court declared the law unconstitutional. The decision was appealed to the Supreme Court of the United States and the case was argued before the Court in Washington on March 5, 1931. Two months later on May 18, the Supreme Court rendered a decision up-holding the constitutionality of the Indiana Chain Store Tax Law. The ruling was a great victory for the independent retailers of Indiana.

On a national level the Capper-Kelly Fair Trade Bill faced a decade of defeat and the legislative committee of the IPhA did not fair much better. A turning point for fair trade legislation occurred in a 1936 Supreme Court hearing. On December 2nd of the same year, the United States Supreme Court rendered a decision up-holding the constitutionality of fair trade laws in Illinois and California. With the success of the Illinois and California laws, the National Association of Retail Druggists (NARD) drafted a Model State Fair Trade Bill for State associations to propose to their legislators. During the 1937 Indiana General Assembly, senate bill number 23 was introduced by Senators Sohl, Post, and Eichhorn, all of Lake County. The bill was then referred to the Judiciary B. committee for a recommendation. The legislative committee conferred with the Judiciary B. committee and deemed it appropriate to substitute the NARD Model State Fair Trade Bill for the original draft proposed by the Senators. Following the substitution, Senator Wade, who chaired the committee, recommended to the Senate that the bill pass. It passed the Senate on February 8th and with an attentive eye from legislative committee chairman A.C. Fritz, the bill passed through the House without an amendment. The Governor signed the bill on February 23, 1937, giving Indiana a law nearly seven months before the passing of the Federal Miller Tydings Act on August 3 of the same year. The Miller Tydings Act enabled the State laws to function within the provisions of the Sherman Anti-Trust Act. The legislative committee of A.C. Fritz, Cecil Gough, Fred Thomas, Stewart Hice, and Kiefer Elliott was praised by the entire association for their efforts in procuring the Model Fair Trade Law. President A.J. Daugherty of South Bend stated that, "There is a feeling of real celebration. The achievement of your association during the late session of the Legislature is something to feel good about." Daugherty also stated the "Twenty-five years of work is now beginning to show results" and that, "The Fair Trade Bill was our baby from the beginning and that had it not been for our efforts the outcome would have been hard to guess."[12] Indeed, the IPhA followed the advice of its president and celebrated. April 1st through the 7th 1937 was declared "Appreciation Week" for the efforts of the legislative committee and all those involved in passing Indiana's Fair Trade Law.

The Flood of 1937 and the Relocation of the Headquarters

The cover of the February 1937 issue of *The Indiana Pharmacist* displayed a picture of submerged store fronts in the center of the business district of New Albany with a small passage that read:

AN EXPLANATION

This issue of *The Indiana Pharmacist* appears without its usual identifying cover and approximately ten days later than usual and in our explanation for the appearance and delay we offer the much used excuse "caused by the flood."

The Indiana Pharmacist is printed by the Floyd County Printing Company at New Albany, located on the basement floor of the Elsby Building, which was badly flooded as water reached the height of 8 feet on the main floor.

The printer was successful in moving some stock, but failed to save any cuts belonging to *The Indiana Pharmacist* and we find that the wood backs of all cuts are so warped that they can not be straightened and we had no opportunity to have new ones made for this issue.[13]

In January 1937, torrential rains were responsible for nineteen inches of precipitation in the Ohio River Valley. The February issue of *The Indiana Pharmacist* listed several members of the association who had been affected by the flooding. The IPhA estimated that the flood had damaged $112,000 dollars worth of merchandise in twenty-five Indiana drugstores. An additional ten drugstores incurred damages to equipment.

In response to the first week of flooding, President Daugherty called an emergency meeting of the Executive Committee at Indianapolis to assess the damage of the flood and create a plan of action to help their fellow pharmacists. It was decided during the meeting that two letters should be drafted; the first was to be sent to all the registered pharmacists in the state soliciting money for the relief effort and the second was to be sent to manufacturers explaining the situation and asking for their help by replacing damaged merchandise.

Business District, New Albany, February 1937

Daugherty appointed A.C. Fritz as the chairman of the relief committee. Fritz and others used the State Board of Pharmacy's mailing lists to expedite the process. Approximately 200 manufacturers received Fritz's letter and nearly all of the manufacturers were eager to replace the goods of their customers or contribute money to the relief effort. The letter to Hoosier retail pharmacists was also a success, resulting in the collection of more than $4,000.

Fritz not only was active in drafting letters soliciting aid but also in visiting the flooded areas to assess damage and provide personal assistance. In one such trip to Jeffersonville – an area where more than fifty percent of the damage to drugstores took place – Fritz was detained by a young deputy "with more of a desire to show authority than to render service." Fritz showed the deputy his credentials and tried explaining to him that he had permission as Chairman of the Relief Committee to access flooded areas. The deputy who was "somewhat deficient in what is known as common sense and with an over supply of ego," ignored Fritz's credentials and hauled him to the sheriff's office. At the station, another sheriff proceeded to "take off his coat and 'beat hell out of Al [Fritz]'."[14]

Temporary quarters of Schreiber Drug Store in Tell City Planing Mill.
Flood January 1937. Tell City, Indiana.

Fritz was at the mercy of the misinformed sheriffs until an experienced railroad detective read his pass and informed the authorities to let him go about his business. After Fritz's ordeal with the sheriff's department, he continued on his journey to visit the stores and store owners of the flooded Jeffersonville, bringing them word of the relief effort and assessing the damages to their property. Fritz retold his ordeal to Secretary McCullough who in turn printed Fritz's mistreatment in *The Indiana Pharmacist.*

Except for A.C. Fritz's unfortunate brush with the authorities, the relief effort was viewed as a large success by the IPhA. It demonstrated an act of solidarity within the profession that transcended a mere gesture of good will. Even though many of the pharmacist affected by the flood were members of the IPhA, the flood relief efforts extended to members and non-members alike. By extending relief efforts to all pharmacists in need, the IPhA demonstrated the purpose of the organization as a caretaker of pharmacy within the State and that the interests of the association were not only for the benefit of its members but all pharmacists.

One year after the flood, the IPhA underwent a change in leadership and also a move of its headquarters from New Albany to Indianapolis. In December of 1937, Frank V. McCullough resigned as secretary of the association, a position that he had held for a decade. The resignation came as a surprise to many in the organization but the vacancy was quickly filled by the executive committee when it appointed Joe L. Weinland of Brazil, Indiana as the new secretary. The change in secretary prompted the IPhA to reevaluate the utility of having the headquarters in New Albany. In January of 1938, the executive committee decided to move IPhA headquarters to Indianapolis due to its central location and close proximity to the new secretary. The headquarters was briefly housed at 806 Test Building located on the Circle in Indianapolis until it was moved to larger accommodations in the same building with two private offices and a reception area. The added space and furnishings provided the needed accommodations for the association's membership activities and increased amount of work for the Fair Trade directories.

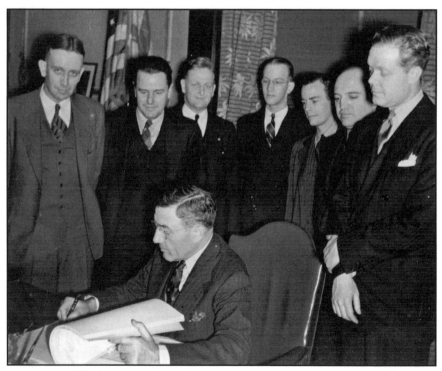

Governor M. Clifford Townsend (seated) signed the Indiana Food & Drug Law on March 6, 1939. IPhA Secretary J. L. Weinland (third from right) present during signing ceremony.

Conclusion

The legislative efforts of the IPhA from 1918 through 1940 were consistent with the national trends of the profession. While its efforts were not especially innovative, the association was effective in preventing unfavorable legislation as was passed in other states, and it even passed some legislation in advance of Federal legislation on many important matters. The IPhA was successful in lobbying for legislation during prohibition to garner exclusivity and responsibility for the profession. During the Depression, the association was also successful in its efforts to procure a Fair Trade Law to help the independent retail pharmacist in the State.

Establishing a full time headquarters was an important step in establishing a position of permanence for the organization. Not only did the full time office meet the administrative needs of the organization, but it also demonstrated the commitment and responsibility of the association to its members and all Hoosier pharmacists. Fostered by the IPhA, pharmacy had raised its status as a profession in Indiana.

Section 3 Endnotes

1 "Vote to Make Indiana Dry," *New York Times*, February 3, 1917, 8.

2 Pete Honorof, "Prohibition and Pharmacy", *The Indiana Pharmacist*, 2 no. 8 (1920), 5.

3 Ibid., 5.

4 Ibid., 5.

5 "Was it Worth it", *The Indiana Pharmacist*, 5 no. 3 (1923), 5.

6 "Principles of Pharmaceutical Ethics", *The Indiana Pharmacist*, 4 no. 11 (1922), 1.

7 Ibid., 1.

8 "Some 1931 Observations", *The Indiana Pharmacist*, 14 no. 1 (1932), 1.

9 "Growth of Chain Stores", *The Indiana Pharmacist*, 4 no. 3 (1922), 3.

10 "Department of Commerce Bureau of the Census", *The Indiana Pharmacist*, 14 no. 9 (1932), 7.

11 "Chain Store Tax", *The Indiana Pharmacist*, 13 no. 6 (1931), 42.

12 "Let's Celebrate – Let's Pause and Consider", *The Indiana Pharmacist*, 19 no. 2 (1937), 8.

13 "An Explanation", *The Indiana Pharmacist*, 19 no. 2 (1937).

14 "Druggists Relief Chairman Detained by Dumb Deputy", *The Indiana Pharmacist*.

LICENSED PHARMACY
TO COMPOUND PRESCRIPTIONS
AND SELL DRUGS

TO SAFEGUARD HEALTH

Member
INDIANA
PHARMACEUTICAL
ASSOCIATION
1940-1970

*World War II
and the
Emergence of
Modern
Pharmacy*

From the beginning of WWII through the 1960's pharmaceutical manufacturing experienced a precipitous increase. Howard Florey's revolutionary work during WWII in isolating penicillin and seeking means to manufacture the drug in the United States saved numerous lives. Other medical breakthroughs such as cortisone, prontosil, and vaccines for viral disease were all mass produced for dispensing at local pharmacies. The influx of pharmaceutical manufacturing provided the foundation for pharmacy to flourish following WWII.

During WWII, the IPhA was an active participant in State and local Civilian Defense Programs. The Legislative Committee of the IPhA supported a national Pharmacy Corps Bill that provided for pharmacists to be commissioned in the United States Army to manage the dispensing of drugs to American soldiers. The IPhA also kept its members at home informed about their fellow pharmacists overseas with sections in *The Indiana Pharmacist* titled "They Are Serving", "Gold Star Honor Roll", and "Letters from Abroad."

During the 1950's the national economy increased and opponents of Fair Trade laws rallied around the charge of price fixing. The IPhA maintained its supportive stance even though many across the nation were becoming disenchanted with Fair Trade laws. In 1952, members of the Hospital Pharmacy Section of the IPhA established the Indiana Society of Hospital Pharmacists as a separate entity.

The 1960's were accompanied by debates about state and federal medical care for the needy and the merit of generic drugs in place of brand names. Senator Estes Kefauver held hearings that investigated the practices of the pharmaceutical industry and the cost of medicine. Following the hearings, the Kefauver – Harris amendment to the Federal Food, Drug, and Cosmetic Act was signed into law providing the drugs must be both safe and effective. In sum, the dramatic changes in the pharmaceutical industry and health policy during the decades following the second World War largely shaped the practice of modern pharmacy.

Contributions of the IPhA during World War II

Pharmacy in Indiana underwent considerable changes during WWII. Overall sales were increased throughout the State. Even before America entered into the war, the U.S. Department of Commerce indicated a five percent increase in sales for Indiana pharmacies from 1939 to 1940.[1] Furthermore, the Indiana Bureau of Census reported a thirteen percent increase in sales from 1940 to 1941, a twenty-six percent increase in sales from 1942 to 1943, and a seven percent increase from 1944 to 1945.[2] The war efforts also created a shortage of pharmacists in Indiana. *The Indiana Pharmacist* reported that a questionnaire distributed in 1942 revealed that of approximately 3600 pharmacists that responded, only 58 registered pharmacists were available for full-time drugstore duty and 116 were available for weekend and part-time duty. The Education Committee of the IPhA collaborated with Dean Jenkins of Purdue University School of Pharmacy to accelerate the four-year curriculum to a three-year program without summer break, in order to accommodate the demands for the war. The committee printed and distributed booklets titled, "Your Future in Pharmacy" for high school students in Indiana to increase interest in the profession. The Education Committee also supported the merging of the Indianapolis College of Pharmacy with Butler University and was active in fundraising for new pharmacy and science buildings at Butler.

The Indiana Pharmacist created new sections and advertisements in support of the war effort. A section named "They are Serving" updated Hoosiers on how many Indiana pharmacists were serving during the war. The first of these printed in May of 1942 listed 60 Hoosier pharmacists contributing to the war effort; by February of 1945, the list had grown to 451 names. *The Indiana Pharmacist* also included a section called "Gold Star Honor Roll" that recognized those pharmacists who had fallen during the war as well as letters from pharmacists overseas. Advertisements filled the journal encouraging pharmacists to sell war stamps and encourage patrons to contribute to the war effort by purchasing war bonds. A dramatic indication of reoriented priorities caused by the war is the cancellation of IPhA annual meetings in 1943 and 1945. Of the many changes that were taking place during the war years, the IPhA was involved in two areas that specifically affected the war efforts at home and abroad. The Civilian Defense Program was fully supported by the association and required the aid of Hoosier pharmacists in instances of domestic emergency. The IPhA was active in aiding the organization of the program and used *The Indiana Pharmacist* as a means to inform Hoosier pharmacists about the progress of the organization. The Legislative Committee of the IPhA was active in lobbying for passage of a

Federal Pharmacy Corps Bill that would establish a branch of the U.S. Army dedicated to managing the drugs and medicines distributed to American Soldiers.

During the 1941 meeting of the Indiana General Assembly, a State Defense Act was adopted providing for the creation of an advisory defense council, administrative defense council, defense fund, and defense housing projects. The Administrative Defense Council was designed to work in cooperation with the federal government and local county defense units to promote national and state defense and implement the state defense program. A facet of the state defense plan that was of particular interest to the IPhA was the office of Chief of Emergency Medical Services. In Indiana the office was held by the State Health Commissioner Dr. John W. Ferree and assisting him was a Medical Advisory Council consisting of member's from the Medical, Dental, Hospital Nurse, Pharmaceutical, Red Cross, and Mortician Associations. In response to dozens of letters from Hoosier pharmacists volunteering their expertise and facilities to the Civilian Defense Program, the IPhA submitted the Emergency Aid Station Plan to the Indiana Chief of Emergency Medical Service in January 1942. The proposal was a fifteen point plan, based on a model drafted by the District of Columbia Pharmaceutical Association which designated drugstores as emergency aid stations. The plan required that all Hoosier drugstores keep a set amount of equipment, supplies, and drugs in stock at all times and that at least one individual working in the drugstore attend a formal course in first aid. The proposed plan stated that during emergency situations the drugstores would act as refuges for the sick and injured and as a social center for disseminating public health information. Other duties of the emergency aid stations included the administering of emergency treatments, conversion of delivery trucks to ambulances, and promotion of preventative health medicines.

On January 19, 1942 Ferree issued a memorandum to all the County Civilian Defense Directors announcing the appointment of County Chiefs of Emergency Medical Services. They would work with a local advisory committee comprised of health professionals to manage medical emergencies on the county level. To assist in this process, the IPhA submitted a list of members organized by the county that the County Chiefs could choose to represent the IPhA on the local Medical Advisory Council.

The Emergency Aid Station plan was not officially accepted in Ferree's memorandum, however, he did include recommendations to the IPhA for pharmacist participation in the Civilian Defense Program. The drugstore was designated as an information center, depot for emergency supplies, and refuge for emergency medical treatment until a patient could be transferred to a hospital, Casualty Station, or First Aid Post. Ferree also included a list of recommended supplies and pharmaceuticals to be stored in the drugstore separate from the retail stock. The IPhA emphasized the importance of the drugstore as an information center and that medical treatment should only be administered during emergency situations.

By May of 1942, Ferree had appointed a County Chief of Emergency Medical Services for each county in Indiana and the local Civilian Defense offices were organized preparing for duties.[3] The IPhA collaborated with Ferree's office to send out a "Manual for Pharmacists in Civilian Defense" prepared and published by the APhA and approved by the U.S. Office of Civilian Defense. The manual was sent to all members of the IPhA encouraging them to sign and return the enclosed pledge form stating that their pharmacy could be used as a Pharmaceutical Unit in the Civilian Defense Program and that the pharmacists pledge their full support and service to the local Chief of Emergency Medical Services. Pharmacists who signed and returned the pledge were sent a placard by the IPhA designating their pharmacy as an official Pharmaceutical Unit in Indiana.

All men between the age of 21 and 36 were eligible for conscription into the United States Army following the passage of the Selective Training and Service Act in 1940. The draft age was changed once the U.S. officially entered the war, so that all males from age 18 to 65 were required to register and those age 18 to 45 were eligible for conscription. When drafted, pharmacists were classified by local draft boards as having specialized training suitable for specific branches of the Army. The IPhA reminded Indiana pharmacists to explicitly state that the individual was a "graduate pharmacist" on all draft questionnaires. A local draft board granted deferments to pharmacists who were the principal support for one or more dependents, who did not meet physical requirements, or who were considered a "necessary man" within the community.[4]

**REMEMBER
PEARL HARBOR!**

FOR
DEFENSE

☆

BUY DEFENSE
BONDS

☆

Sell Defense
Savings
Stamps
In Your
Store

☆

This Space Donated by The Indiana Pharmacist

The Indiana Pharmacist, February, 1942

The Federal Government defined a "necessary man" as an individual whose vocation was "essential to the national health, safety, or interest in the sense that a serious interruption or delay in such activity is likely to impede the national defense program."[5] A pharmacist deemed a "necessary man" was granted a deferment of six months and had to reapply for an additional deferment after the six months had expired. Pharmacists who were the sole proprietors and operators of a drugstore were often deemed "necessary men" by their local draft boards.

Pharmacists who were drafted and met stringent requirements for pharmaceutical education, training, and ability as well as administrative ability and proficiency for Army work were eligible for commission as a second lieutenant in the Medical Administrative Corps. Pharmacists so commissioned were initially enlisted for active duty for a period of one year that could be extended with the consent of the pharmacist. Once the U.S. officially entered WWII, the length of service was extended to six months after the war had concluded. After their term of service, pharmacists enlisting as commissioned officers were allowed to return to civilian life while maintaining their commission on the reserve list.

Officers in the Medical Administrative Corps were assigned commissions as hospital administration, mess management, supervisors of hospital records, and supervisors of medical supplies. Pharmacists who did not qualify for officer training were designated the ranks of private and assigned to duties "not of a pharmaceutical nature."[6] Pharmacists who wanted to contribute to the Army by providing a more technical service were encouraged to register with the American Red Cross as pharmacy technicians. Pending need and the meeting of certain qualifications, pharmacy technicians could potentially be promoted to technical sergeants. Whether a pharmacist was a commissioned officer, a private, or pharmacy technician for the Red Cross, the Selective Training and Service Act of 1940 mandated that pharmacists concluding their term of service "must be restored by his former employer to his position or a similar one with the same seniority, status, and pay."[7]

The United States entrance into WWII required plans for the medical treatment of the American soldiers. Members of Congress, along with national and state pharmaceutical associations, stressed the importance of American soldiers receiving the same protection granted to American civilians in respect to drugs and medicine. On July 24, 1942, Representative Carl T. Durham of North Carolina introduced H.R. 7432 to the United States House of Representatives to provide for the establishment of a Pharmacy Corps in the U.S. Army. A companion bill was introduced to the Senate ten days later by Senator Robert R. Reynolds of North Carolina, Chairman of the Senate Military Affairs Committee. The IPhA strongly supported the Pharmacy Corps Bill and urged Hoosier pharmacists to write Representative Forest A. Harness of Kokomo, Indiana, representing the 5th Indiana Congressional District to demonstrate their support for the bill. Harness like Reynolds was a member of the Military Affairs Committee of the House of Representatives.

Those in favor of the Pharmacy Corps bill were concerned that the Army would permit the compounding of drugs and medicines by enlisted men who had received only a 90 – day instructional course, at best. Congressman Durham stated, "The modern treatment of disease requires the use of such highly specialized, complex compounds as sulfanilamide, sulfathiazole, sulfadiazine, and sulfaguanidine, and serums, vaccines, and antitoxins. These very effective new drugs have greatly changed the procedure of the Army doctor; no longer does he confine his prescribing to the drugs found in the simple lists of a few years ago. The safety of our men in uniform demands that those who handle these drugs and similar medicines be highly-trained, competent individuals who are familiar with the character of the potent substances they supply."[8]

Durham's bill proposed that the National Defense Act of June 3, 1916 be amended to change the name of the Medical Administrative Corps to the Pharmacy Corps. The proposed bill would increase the number of personnel in the Corps from 16 pharmacists to 72 and provided a new promotion schedule for those individuals in the Corps. The bill also proposed as an amendment to the National Defense Act to give the pharmacists similar rights and privileges to individuals enlisted in the Medical, Dental, and Veterinary Corps.

The Pharmacy Corps Bill was scheduled for a hearing on March 2, 1943, in response the IPhA drafted a letter requesting that all members living in the Fifth Congressional District notify Representative Harness of their support for the bill. The Legislative Committee of the IPhA collaborated with State Senator Daviess A. Batterton, a Greensburg pharmacist, and Representative Posey Cooper, a Sellersburg pharmacist, to introduce a joint resolution by the Indiana Legislature urging Congress to pass the Pharmacy Corps Bill. The resolution was unanimously adopted by the Indiana Senate with concurrence by the Indiana House making it one of the first six states in the Nation to adopt such a resolution.[9]

The Pharmacy Corps Joint Resolution adopted by the Indiana Legislature was directed to the attention of the President of the United States Senate, the Speaker of the House of Representatives, the President of the United States, the Secretary of War, the Surgeon-General of the United States Army, and to the

Members of Congress.[10] On July 12 1943, President Roosevelt signed the Pharmacy Corp Bill into law. The original bill was amended by the Senate Committee on Military Affairs on July 3rd to establish the Pharmacy Corps as a separate entity from the Medical Administrative Corps. When the bill was signed by President Roosevelt, the 16 pharmacists and 42 non- pharmacists who comprised the Medical Administrative Corps were transferred to the Pharmacy Corps, and an additional 72 pharmacists that were added by the act. The Pharmacy Corps thus consisted of the 130 men until death, reassignment, or resignation reduced the Corps to the 72 pharmacists originally intended for by the bill.

A New Professionalism and the End of Fair Trade in Indiana

The end of WWII saw the national economy continue to rise and a reinvigorated sense of professionalism within pharmacy. According to the annual report of the National Association of Retail Druggists (NARD) in 1946, Fair Trade laws prevented pharmaceutical prices from increasing by more than one percent throughout the war. With the war over and the economy continuing to flourish, many merchants throughout the nation became disenchanted with Fair Trade laws and the opponents of Fair Trade mounted attacks against the laws rallying around the charge of price fixing. The NARD represented the interests of the retail pharmacists on the national level by continuing its staunch support of Fair Trade laws. Through the 1950's the constitutionality of Fair Trade laws was challenged in Indiana and other states. Even though the IPhA continued to support Fair Trade, the challenges on the business front engendered a renewed sense of professionalism within the association.

The value of the IPhA to Hoosier pharmacists during the war effort was reflected by growth in its annual membership. Harold Darnell executive secretary of the IPhA reported a record high of 1,095 active members at the association's annual meeting of 1946.[11] Even with the cancellation of the 1943 and 1945 annual meetings, membership had continued to increase. This growth paralleled activities in Indiana to increase professional development. The Pharmacy Schools at Purdue and Butler held regular conferences on professional pharmacy. In 1952, the IPhA adopted a new code of ethics that was drafted by the APhA at its centennial convention. *The Indiana Pharmacist* added a section titled "Modern Pharmaceutical Practices" that discussed the merits of antibiotics, insulin, and disease-state treatments. Furthermore, the association challenged its members to consider the future of the IPhA as more than a trade association, suggesting it should have equal standing with the other professional organizations.

In May of 1951 the United States Supreme Court ruled that the Miller-Tydings Act was unconstitutional and that the Federal Government did not have the authority to authorize price fixing on goods moving in interstate commerce. This ruling rendered state Fair Trade laws essentially ineffective. In response to the decision, the IPhA collaborated with the NARD, other State associations, Indiana wholesalers, and Indiana drugstore chains to find the means to defend the principles of Fair Trade and avoid price-wars. Manufacturers with business ties to Indiana were contacted and the IPhA was assured that the manufacturers would do everything legally possible to uphold the principles of Fair Trade. While the decision of the Supreme Court did not repeal the State laws, individual States could not enforce "non-signer" clauses which forced all merchants to maintain the minimum price of a manufactured good so long as one store signed a Fair Trade agreement with the manufacturer of said good.

It did not take long for proponents of Fair Trade to draft new federal legislation to enable the State laws. In November of 1951 H.R. 5767 was introduced to the House of Representatives by John A. McGuire of Connecticut. In the spring of 1952, President Truman signed the McGuire Bill into law once again enabling State Fair Trade Laws and enforcement of the "non-signer" clause. Similar to the Miller-Tydings Act, the McGuire Act allowed States to pass price fixing legislation without infringing on the Federal Sherman Anti-Trust laws. The IPhA announced the return of Fair Trade in the August issue of *The Indiana Pharmacist* in 1952. The article reminded Hoosier pharmacists about the validity of prior Fair Trade agreements with manufacturers and the opportunities to sign new contracts under the provision of the law.

Hoosier pharmacists reaped the benefits of the State Association's staunch support of Fair Trade laws until October of 1955, when an Indiana court rendered the Indiana Fair Trade law unconstitutional in a case involving the

IPhA promotes professionalism and advancement of the profession.

Bissell Carpet Sweeper Company. Bissell appealed the decision to the Indiana Supreme Court and in 1957 the Court ruled that the "non-signer" clause was unconstitutional rendering the State Fair Trade Act ineffective. The IPhA maintained its firm support of Fair Trade and urged its members to maintain the principles of Fair Trade within the State. Even though the Indiana Fair Trade Act was still effective, without the "non-signer" clause, there were few benefits for Hoosier pharmacists to sign an agreement with a manufacturer. Without the "non-signer" clause, the era of Fair Trade in Indiana came to a close.

The battles for Fair Trade following the end of WWII were accompanied by a renewed sense of professionalism for Indiana pharmacy. Whether it was a reaction to the association's struggles for Fair Trade or an earnest reassessment of its duties to advance the profession, the IPhA was devoted to increasing the professional prominence of Hoosier pharmacy. This was spelled out near the end of WWII, when *The Indiana Pharmacist* posed a series of questions to its readers:

> What are your plans for your postwar drugstore? Are you going to swing more to the professional side of the drug business, or farther away from it? Are you going in for fast merchandising, or going to learn more and more to [about] exclusive pharmaceutical service? Are you going to enlarge and expand, or remodel your present quarters? Are you going to have a soda fountain, or exclude it? What type of business are you going after, and what types of competition are you expecting to have to meet?[12]

The IPhA wanted its members to consider the future of their business, the association, and the profession in a post war era.

In 1956, *The Indiana Pharmacist*, published an address by Madeline Oxford Holland, editor of the *American Professional Pharmacists*, titled "Our State Associations – TRADE OR PROFESSIONAL?" The article was prefaced by an editor's note stating that IPhA needed to refocus its efforts in professional matters to obtain official recognition as a profession. The article acknowledged pressures created by the Great Depression which forced Hoosier pharmacists to replace many professional interests with commercial pursuits. For example, to supplement the sale of drugs, arrays of merchandise from candy to household gadgets were available for purchase in the drugstore. The supplemental income from the sale of such items availed the pharmacist to sustain their business. Understandably, the IPhA also reflected the concerns of its membership. While the IPhA maintained the importance of professional development, its priority was to safeguard the financial security of its membership. Most notable, the association's lobbying and support for Fair Trade laws reflected the business conscious pharmacists it represented.

Holland stated in her address that the time had come for pharmacy to seek a balance between sound business practice and the advancement of professionalism. It was the duty of the State Association to facilitate professional advancement by promoting professional and scientific papers within the organization, demonstrating professionalism through sound leadership and example, and actively involve the organization in the health of the public.

Members of the IPhA who took the lead in the professional and scientific advancement of pharmacy were the Hoosier hospital pharmacists. In 1946, the Indiana Hospital Act was promulgated, making Indiana one of the first three states licensing hospital pharmacy services, space, storage, and labeling.[13] On July 28, 1949, under the leadership of Edward J. Wolfgang of Evansville, the hospital pharmacists founded the Hospital Pharmacy Section of the IPhA. The objectives of the Hospital Pharmacy Section were:

> To develop closer relationship between the hospital pharmacists of Indiana and the Indiana Pharmaceutical Association.
>
> To improve the status of pharmacists in the hospitals of the State.
>
> To improve and develop the effectiveness of the pharmacist in the hospital.
>
> To better pharmaceutical service in hospitals.
>
> To improve relationship between the pharmacist and other hospital staff.
>
> To promote sound, efficient, and economical administration of the hospital pharmacy.
>
> To assist in educational programs of the hospital.[14]

The Hospital Pharmacy Section of the IPhA remained part of the association for only three years after its founding. In 1952 the Hospital Pharmacy Section officially separated from the IPhA to establish the Indiana Society of Hospital Pharmacists (ISHP). Allen V.R. Beck of Indianapolis was chairman of the ISHP and oversaw the departure from the IPhA and establishment of an Indiana Chapter of the American Society of Hospital Pharmacists later the same year. The primary reason for the section's departure from the IPhA was the expectation that the ISHP as a separate entity could better serve the members of its society by primarily focusing on institutional practice.

The Kefauver Drug Hearings

During the early 1960's the expansion of the pharmaceutical industry accelerated. In 1960 drug manufacturers were providing jobs three times faster than other areas of manufacturing and growing in dollar volume twice as fast as the national economy.[15] Employment had increased in drug manufacturing by 27% over totals in 1947. Other manufacturers displayed only a 5.7% increase. Retail pharmacists were pleased that wholesale prices declined by 6% during the same period while other commodities were rising by 18.9%.[16]

Issues that concerned Hoosier pharmacists included the increase of the pharmacy school curriculum to a five year degree, use of generic drugs, federal and state medical insurance, and increasing working relations with nursing home facilities. State and federally provided medical care by way of the Indiana Welfare Medical Program, Medicare, and Medicaid changed the dynamic by which pharmacists received payments and negotiated the price for prescriptions. The Indiana Welfare Medical Program began in 1961 and provided medical care for the needy and individuals over the age of 65 who had insufficient income. Don Newman, a member of the IPhA from Mishawaka, proposed a pricing schedule for government paid prescriptions in an article submitted to *The Indiana Pharmacist* in 1960. Newman stated that his plan "embodies recognition of a principle long overdue: that pharmacists be recognized as professionals, and as such be entitled to a professional fee!"[17] Newman followed his point with a quote from Senator Hubert H. Humphrey's 1960 speech before Congress: "a pharmacist is more than a purveyor of drugs – he is a member of a team of experts who have been scientifically trained to provide medical care to the people."[18] Newman followed the Senator's quote with one of his own, "To live up to the term will take us many years, to grow up to the term can start today."[19]

Both the government and the general public desired cheaper pharmaceuticals, such as substituting generic drugs for more expensive name-brand goods. Physicians helped by prescribing them to their patients. Government health insurance and generic drugs both played a significant role in the pharmacist's relationship with nursing homes. The residents of nursing homes were eligible for medical care under the Indiana Welfare Medical Program and the government determined the most cost effective way to provide drugs for the residents.

The Kefauver Drug Hearings of 1959 echoed the concerns of generic drug supporters by investigating practices of the pharmaceutical industry and the cost of medicines. Senator Estes Kefauver of Tennessee presided over the hearings and expanded the investigation to include advertisement abuses and questionable drug efficacy. Following the hearings, Kefauver proposed a bill to increase regulation of the pharmacy industry that eventually stalled in congress.

The aftermath from the Kefauver drug hearings initiated numerous responses from members of the IPhA. John V. Bothel of Lafayette wrote that,

Executive Committee at Annual Convention, French Lick, Indiana, 1964. Front row from left to right: Earl Triplett, Charles A. Schreiber, Thurman Miller, and Roy Haney. Back row from left to right: Maurie Keltsch, Joseph E. McSoley, William Long, Merritt Skinner, and Frank Reeves.

"The Kefauver smear tactics used before Congressional Committees has promoted an erroneous idea that the use of generic names will gain the consumer lower cost medication."[20] In an article titled "Interprofessional Strength", the IPhA stated that the Kefauver hearings created a need for Indiana to reassess the cost of Welfare medicine but that that the hearings were the "opening gun of a long planned attack against private medical and pharmaceutical services."[21] The association's attitude towards the Kefauver hearings is best summarized by Gene Hinshaw during his president's address during the 1960 annual convention:

> Then there were the Kefauver Hearings. I won't, or rather can't, reveal my feelings concerning him and his cohorts. First, this address was printed in *The Indiana Pharmacist* which is mailed. And I can't speak now – because there are ladies present. I am glad, tho[ugh], for the people of Tennessee, that the dear Senator is not an M.D., specializing as a diagnostician! Can't you just guess what would happen when he starts to interpret the results of a week of test and x-rays on some patient? He'd probably tell them they would have to have their Arteriosclerosis cut off and amputated, they've got Auto-intoxication from riding in Compact Cars and have intestinal putrefaction due to hepatic insufficiency.[22]

On September 12, 1960 the William S. Merrell Company of Cincinnati submitted a new drug application to the FDA for Kevadon. Kevadon was the brand name of a thalidomide sedative that had been marketed in Europe since 1956. The FDA denied the application because of incomplete data to support the safety of the drug. In November of 1961 Germany pulled the drug off of the market because of its association with congenital birth defects. Even though the FDA did not approve Kevadon, the William S. Merrell Company distributed the drug to over 1,000 physicians for investigational use. Over 20,000 Americans received thalidomide from the physicians, including 624 pregnant patients that resulted in 17 known congenital abnormalities.[23]

Following the thalidomide tragedy, Senator Kefauver and U.S. Representative Oren Harris of Arkansas revived their languishing bill to require manufacturers to prove the safety and efficacy of drugs prior to FDA approval. John F. Kennedy signed the bill into law on October 10, 1962. The Kefauver – Harris Amendment to the Federal Food, Drug, and Cosmetic Act was the first law to test the effectiveness of pharmaceuticals.

Important legislation –whether favorable or detrimental to the interests of the organization – the IPhA typically printed a full page article in *The Indiana Pharmacist* explaining the new legislation and its effect on the current practices within the State. Following the passage of the Kefauver – Harris Amendment, a small article surrounded by three large advertisements was printed that outlined the provisions of the law. The scant fanfare reflected acceptance of reality rather than approval or disapproval.

Conclusion

The rise of the pharmacy industry during the 1950's and 1960's engendered new struggles for the IPhA. Issues with health insurance and generic drugs persisted in subsequent years. The renewed sense of professionalism that Hoosier pharmacists incurred following WWII continued to gain momentum through the 1960's and provided impetus for pharmacy to stand among the ranks of the other professions. The IPhA would have to remain diligent in the years to come to ensure the well-being of Hoosier pharmacists in a changing health system. Despite, or perhaps because of, increasing federal government interest in healthcare, as well as changes in the industry, pharmacists continued to see the value of a professional organization like the IPhA to promote their interests.

Section 4 Endnotes

1 "State Drug Store Sales Increase 5% in 1940", *The Indiana Pharmacist,* 23 no. 2 (1941), 38.

2 "Retail Sales Report October, 1941", *The Indiana Pharmacist,* 24 no. 1 (1942), 20.

"Retail Sales Report April, 1943", *The Indiana Pharmacist,* 25 no. 6 (1943), 255.

3 "County Emergency Medical Chiefs Appointed", *The Indiana Pharmacist* , 24 no. 5 (1942), 146.

4 "If Your 21 to 36", *The Indiana Pharmacist,* 23 no. 2 (1941), 33.

5 Ibid., 33.

6 Ibid., 34.

7 Ibid., 34.

8 "Pharmacy Corps in Army Asked", *The Indiana Pharmacist,* 24 no. 8 (1942), 266.

9 "Resolution of the Indiana State Legislature", *The Indiana Pharmacist,* 25 no. 3 (1943), 74.

10 "Legislative Activities", *The Indiana Pharmacist,* 25 no. 6 (1943), 217.

11 "Proceedings of the Indiana Pharmaceutical Association", *The Indiana Pharmacist,* 28 no. 8 (1946), 5.

12 "Modernizing to Meet Competition", *The Indiana Pharmacist,* 27 no. 8 (1945), 263.

13 J.H. Jones, *The Monthly Bulletin of the Indiana State Board of Health,* 1963.

14 "Hospital Pharmacy Section of IPhA Organized", *The Indiana Pharmacist,* 31no. 9 (1949), 249.

15 "Growth, Sales, and Profits in Drug Industry", *The Indiana Pharmacist,* 42 no. 6 (1960), 189.

16 Ibid., 189.

17 "Issues and Compromises we Face in the Indiana Welfare Medical Program", *The Indiana Pharmacist,* 42 no.10 (1960), 295.

18 Ibid., 295.

19 Ibid., 295.

20 "Pharmacy Recent News", *The Indiana Pharmacist,* 42 no. 9 (1960), 283.

21 "Interprofessional Strength", *The Indiana Pharmacist,* 42 no. 9 (1960), 209.

22 "President's Address", *The Indiana Pharmacist,* 42 no. 9 (1960), 173.

23 "The History Drug Regulation in the United States", www.fda.org.

Pharmacy in a Changing Health Environment

Healthcare in America has undergone rapid change since the 1970s, and the IPhA responded in several ways to assist its member's needs. Examples of these changes include a new consumerism, increased government regulation, and reform of health insurance. The IPhA itself underwent reorganization and administrative changes during this period both in response to these external developments as well as internal ones.

The 1970's marked the beginning of a new age in consumerism. In pharmacy that meant patients wanted to know more about the medicines they were purchasing and how they could be purchased in the most cost effective manner. The IPhA maintained that an informed consumer is a good consumer, the type of consumer with which pharmacists wanted to do business. The association promoted open communication with the consumer about the services that pharmacists provided. Counseling patients about costs, the side effects, and special instructions for a patient's medication became increasingly important in addition to explaining the pharmacist's duties about patient profiles, mindfulness of drug interactions, emergency hours, and delivery services. In short, the IPhA wanted pharmacists to gain the confidence of consumers by explaining the merits of the pharmacy and its role in the health field. Patient consulting became an important facet of the pharmacist-consumer relationship and "clinical pharmacy" proliferated across the state.

The increased government oversight and reform of health insurance engendered new issues in a changing health care environment. Emerging from the 1960's was the issue of Medicare and third-party payment and the professional fee for prescription pricing. The national sentiment that health was the birthright of every citizen created a greater need for private and government funded insurance programs. As Fair Trade had been the business concern for pharmacists in the 30's, 40's, and 50's, concerns with third-party payment became a prominent issue for the IPhA in subsequent decades.

During the seventies, eighties, and nineties, the IPhA underwent numerous organizational changes while maintaining its commitment to professional advancement. Because of new licensing standards in 1974, continuing education (CE) programs became increasingly important and the IPA collaborated with Butler and Purdue Universities to produce many CE television programs for Hoosier pharmacists. In 1975, Barbara Nelson became the first woman to be elected president of the association. In the same year, Nelson was appointed by Governor Otis R. Bowen to serve on the Indiana State Board of Pharmacy as well. Nelson was a pioneer in Hoosier pharmacy, paving the way for women pharmacists that would follow her. At the time of her election and appointment, 47% of the students attending the Purdue University School of Pharmacy were women.

In 1979, the IPhA changed its name to the Indiana Pharmacists Association (IPA). The aims and duties of the organization remained the same, but the name change reflected that the association was *for* the pharmacist. The IPA members also became increasingly involved in drug abuse prevention, speaking at many schools across the state and sponsoring public service announcements.

In 1982, the association celebrated its centennial anniversary with a commemorative issue of *The Indiana Pharmacist*. The issue contained a list of past presidents and executive directors of the association along with a group of pictures titled, "A Pictorial Look at our First 100 Years". There was a note from President Ronald Reagan congratulating the association on 100 years of service and a proclamation from Governor Robert D. Orr declaring May 2 – 9, 1982 as Indiana Pharmacists Week. The issue also contained "A picture resume…forty-five years with IPA" of Mary Lou Byrn, long time secretary and assistant editor of The Indiana Pharmacist; as well as an article highlighting the Schreiber family of Tell City and Schreiber Pharmacy. In 1989, the association established a building fund to buy a building to serve as headquarters for the IPA.

During the 1990's the IPA was very active in the General Assembly, seeking legislation to further define the role of the pharmacist in the healthcare system. For example, in 1995 SB 554 recognized Indiana pharmacists as providers of healthcare, in 1996, SB 414 allowed pharmacists to manage drug therapy for patients in organized health care settings, and in 1997, SB 184 provided health insurance reimbursement to pharmacists for educating diabetic patients on self management. The trend continued in 2007, when the IPA was successful in lobbying for HB 1468, which allowed pharmacists to provide mass flu immunizations under a protocol with a physician. Also in the 1990's, the IPA joined back with the Indiana Society of Health – System Pharmacists to merge into the Indiana Pharmacists Alliance.

A Move for the IPA

In 1989, the IPA Education Foundation created a building fund to provide a new "home for pharmacy" in Indiana.[1] The IPA had a lease on a downtown office in Indianapolis which expired in December of 1992. IPA President

Mary Lou Byrn (1914 – 1998)

IPA staff members Patsy Ettinger Schnabel (L) and Mary Lou Byrn posed with Mrs. Lois Long and William Long, P.D at an IPA banquet in the early 1960's.

Mary Lou Byrn worked as an administrative assistant for the IPA for 48 years. During her time at the IPA she saw the flooding of her home town of New Albany, many moves of the association's headquarters, the rise and fall of Fair Trade, WWII, the fallout from the Kefauver hearings, the boom in pharmaceutical manufacturing, seven executive directors, 46 presidents, hundreds of members, and countless other developments for Hoosier pharmacy. Mary Lou Byrn began working for the IPhA in 1937 at the age of 23. She worked at the first headquarters in New Albany for a year before the move to Indianapolis in1938. During the 30's and 40's, Byrn was heavily involved in Fair Trade paperwork and updating The Indiana Pharmacist with the most recent Fair Trade prices. During WWII Byrn frequently responded to questions about the IPhA's war effort. Throughout her years with the IPA she gained the reputation of a dedicated professional and valued friend. To commemorate her 35th anniversary with the association, the IPA purchased a European Rhine Cruise for Mary Lou in 1972. In 1977, Mary Lou was presented with an honorary life membership in the IPA, the only life membership ever presented to a non-pharmacist. Byrn retired from the IPA in 1984. At the annual meeting that year, she was honored with a retirement luncheon where she was awarded a mantle clock by the Eli Lilly Company and a plaque from the association for her 48 years of service. Following her passing on February 14, 1998, Dave Clark, former Executive Director and friend to Mary Lou described her best as, "Those of you who knew and loved her will miss her a lot! To those of you who didn't know her, you missed a grand lady!"

Shirley Gerhart and Jack Gerhart (left) present a check to Cindy Weil (right) for the Foundation's building fund.

Cindy Weil was the organizer for the building fund. During the midyear retreat of 1989, Weil challenged IPA members to contribute to a building fund to accommodate the growing size, strength, and influence of the association. In addition to soliciting contributions, Weil let her actions speak loudest when she was the first individual to donate to the new building fund. Members that donated more than $5,000 were inducted into the "Hoosier Hall of Fame", those that donated $1,000 - $4,999 were considered "founders", pledges of $500-$999 were considered "cornerstones", pledges of $250 - $499 were "investors", and all pledges below $250 were considered "builders."[2]

During the fall of 1992, the Pharmacists Education Foundation purchased the new home for the IPA at 729 N. Pennsylvania St. in Indianapolis. During January and February of 1993, smaller rooms were removed from the building to provide room for a large board room on the main floor. The IPA officially moved into the new office building on March 6, 1993. An open house and ribbon cutting ceremony was held during the Annual Meeting in September, 1993.

IPA's Involvement in OBRA '90

In 1990, the federal government passed the Omnibus Budget Reconciliation Act (OBRA '90). The law required pharmacies to perform prospective drug utilization reviews (DUR) for patients covered by Medicaid in order to remain compliant with the reimbursement program. It was intended that the prospective DUR would screen for drug allergies, therapeutic duplication, incorrect dosing or duration of treatment, clinical misuse/ abuse, drug-disease contraindication, and drug-drug interaction. The federal government set a deadline of January 1, 1993 for individual states to establish DUR programs.

Early in 1991, the IPA established its Drug Utilization Review Task Force to analyze the DUR programs mandated under OBRA '90. In November of the same year, the DUR Task Force submitted a report to the IPA Board of Directors that outlined a plan to implement a DUR program in Indiana to comply with federal regulations. The plan was used as a basis for House Bill 1337, which provided for a DUR board in Indiana. OBRA '90 required state DUR boards to review drug claim information to analyze trends of fraud, abuse, and overuse, as well as monitor therapeutic appropriateness and over/ under utilization. On February 26, 1992 the diligence of the IPA came to fruition when Governor Bayh signed House Bill 1337 into law. Charles G. Dobis, President of the IPA in 1992, stated that OBRA '90 provided impetus for changing the emphasis of pharmacy practice from "the drugs people take to the people who take drugs".

Later, Governor Evan Bayh appointed Charles O. Rutledge, Ph.D. and Dean of the Purdue School of Pharmacy as the first Chairman of the state Medicaid DUR board.

In 1993, the IPA conducted a series of ten workshops around the state to teach pharmacists how to effectively counsel patients and to explain the impact of OBRA '90 on the everyday practice of pharmacy.

Economic Hardships for the IPA

In September of 1990, IPA President Rhonda Eldridge informed members that the association was essentially broke. In 1989 the IPA lost $58,000 and in eight of the ten prior years the association had annual deficits.[3] In previous years, reserve funds were allocated to make up for the deficit, but as of 1990, the association's reserves were depleted. On September 14, the Board of Directors assumed control of the IPA office when the association was unable to make payroll for the week. On the same day, the Board of Directors named Joseph E. McSoley to serve in an interim Executive Director position. During the five months that the IPA was without an executive director, McSoley provided leadership and service for the organization. McSoley volunteered "much time and tireless effort" to help the organization through the troubled times.[4]

The Board of Directors implemented changes over the course of the next three months in an effort to increase cash flow and improve management of the association. All staff wages and benefits were temporarily frozen in addition to travel and entertainment expenses. The company car was sold, all of the association's credit cards were cancelled, and membership at the Columbia Club was cancelled. The Eli Lilly Company financed and arranged a meeting with the Executive Directors of the Oklahoma and Nebraska Pharmacists Associations and the IPA to discuss the reorganization of the association. Lilly also assigned an accountant to the IPA to create a new accounting system.

On November 20, an Executive Search Committee appointed by President Rhonda Eldridge held an organizational meeting to begin a search for finding a new Executive Director. Five months later, the Board of Directors appointed Lawrence J. Sage as the new Executive Vice President of the IPA. Prior to Sage's appointment, he served as Deputy Director of the Health Professions Bureau where his experience running the daily operations of the agency, including licensure, records, fiscal and data processing divisions made him a suitable choice for the position.[5]

Upon accepting the position, Sage stated that, "My experience as the previous Director of the Board of Pharmacy provided me a unique involvement in some of the issues facing pharmacy and pharmacists today. I have developed an in-depth understanding of administrative rule-making and the legislative process. I believe this understanding will allow me to represent the association's policies and concerns in both of these arenas. I believe that I can be a positive force for growth and change in the Association."[6] Lary Sage was the first non-pharmacist in the history of the association to hold the position of Executive Vice President of the IPA.

The interim director, McSoley, continued to represent Hoosier pharmacists on a daily basis at the Statehouse during the General Assembly of 1991. McSoley refused payment for his services and "conveniently misplaced receipts for any of his out-of-pocket expenses."[7] McSoley, a graduate of Butler University School of Pharmacy, was an independent pharmacy owner in Indianapolis for 37 years. In 1989 he sold McSoley's Pharmacy and retired, but he remained active in the association until his death on July 25, 1996. He had a long and illustrious career in the profession holding numerous positions with state and national associations, committees, and boards. For the IPA he held the positions of President in 1967 and treasurer from 1970 to 1995. McSoley had also served intermittently on the association's Board of Directors starting in 1953.

In 1987, the IPA established the "Joseph E. McSoley Pharmacist of the Year Award" that is presented to a pharmacist who demonstrates long-term commitment and service to the profession of pharmacy and service to the State Association and who has been involved in community and civic affairs.[8] The 1996 winner of the award, Winnie Landis, announced at the annual meeting of the same year that the Pharmacists Education Foundation of the IPA planned to start an annual scholarship to commemorate McSoley's life, legacy, and service to the IPA. In 1998 the "Joseph E. McSoley Scholarship" was presented for the first time at the spring meeting of the IPA. The scholarship was awarded to two students, one from each of the Butler and Purdue schools of pharmacy, who exemplified extraordinary leadership, community involvement, and volunteerism.

Strength through Unification

In 1995 IPA president Bruce A. Hufford and Bill Malatestinic, president of the Indiana Society of Hospital Pharmacists (ISHP) appointed members to a task force to assess the possibility of merging the two organizations. The organizations had worked together on legislative initiatives and planning for a joint annual meeting throughout the year and it was thought by members of both organizations that their mutual interests warranted a merger. For two years the IPA and IHSP conducted quarterly meetings to discuss the logistics of structuring the organization.

In the 1997, July/August issue of *The Indiana Pharmacist*, Lary Sage informed association members that the IPA and ISHP would merge to form the Indiana Pharmacists Alliance (IPA). Sage called it "a new era for the profession in the state."[9] An overwhelming 95% of the votes cast from the two organizations supported the merger. Bruce Clayton, president of the Indiana Pharmacists Association during the merger stated that the collaborative efforts of both organizations created a better opportunity "to advance the practice of ALL pharmacists in Indiana".

On November 9, 1997, officers were installed for the new academies and the Alliance. Dr. Glen Sperandio, a former faculty member at the Purdue School of Pharmacy (1945 -1984) and long time executive director of the ISHP administered the oaths of office to the academy officers and vice presidents and the Alliance officers.[10] On the same day, IPA President Bruce Clayton and ISHP President Francine Breckler signed the legal documents for the IPA-ISHP merger to be filed with the Secretary of State's Office. Following the installation of officers and the signing of the merger papers, Dr. Glen Sperandio was awarded the first Honorary Life Membership by the Alliance Board.

On January 1, 1998 the IPA officially began operations with Bruce Clayton as the first president of the new Alliance. There were four academies under the umbrella of IPA each with its own president:

The Indiana Academy of Community Pharmacists (IACP) – Jan Bopp
The Indiana Society of Health-System Pharmacists (ISHP) – Bruce Carlstedt
The Indiana Society of Consultant Pharmacists (ISCP) – Tina Bauman
The Indiana Academy of Pharmacy Technicians (IAPT) – Jan Henline

The first Board of Directors was made up of Bruce Clayton and the other academy presidents as well as Francine Breckler, President-Elect, Warren Richards, Alliance Treasurer, and Bruce Hufford, Alliance Past-President.

The first annual meeting of the new Alliance was held eight months later on September 11-12, 1998 at the Sheraton Hotel at Keystone at the Crossing in Indianapolis. More than 200 pharmacists, students, and exhibitors attended the meeting.[11]

125 Years Later

As of 2007, there are 1,301 active members in the IPA belonging to one of the four academies each incorporating a specific area of pharmacy: Indiana Academy of Community Pharmacists (IACP), Indiana Society of Health-System Pharmacists (ISHP), Indiana Academy of Long – Term Care Pharmacists (IALTCP), and Indiana Academy of Pharmacy Technicians (IAPT). The association has remained at 729 N. Pennsylvania in Indianapolis since its move in 1993. The IPA employs four full-time staff members: Lawrence J. Sage, Tabitha Cross, Carol Dunham, and Lana Whitecotton.

Lary Sage has remained the Executive Vice President of the Indiana Pharmacists Alliance since 1991. Sage is responsible for all the staff members of the IPA and manages the day-to-day activities of the Alliance. The Executive Vice President cultivates pharmacist leadership in the Alliance for the purpose of advancing pharmacy practice in Indiana and is the primary spokesperson representing pharmacy practice in the state.

Tabitha Cross joined the IPA in June of 2002 and is the Director of Professional Development. Cross is responsible for assessing and promoting professional development opportunities through continuing education programs in conjunction with the Education Council of the Alliance. Cross also oversees the Alliance web site and serves as the Managing Editor for *The Indiana Pharmacist* and the *ImPAct* newsletter.

Carol Dunham has been with the IPA since July of 1990 and is the Alliance Meeting Coordinator. Dunham is responsible for planning and coordination of all Alliance meetings and events. This includes preview, inspection and recommendation of potential sites along with publicizing the events. Carol also oversees the operation of the Pharmacists Recovery Network. Lana Whitecotton, who joined the office staff in 2002, is the Membership Coordinator and maintains membership records.

Conclusion

On May 9, 2007, members of the IPA Board of Directors gathered for a regular meeting and enjoyed cake commemorating the 125th anniversary of the association. It seemed fitting that the meeting was in the McSoley Board Room where a shelved wall contains 125 years of *The Indiana Pharmacist* and other artifacts from the organization's history. As the members enjoyed their cake, one wonders if they considered the men and women of the past whose deeds helped shape the history of the organization and how those at the meeting were not only sharing the celebration with each other, but with those members as well. While the IPA had changed names and headquarters locations over the years and the pertinent issues have changed with the decades, the purpose of the association remains the same – to serve as the state professional organization of pharmacists, representing the pharmacy profession in Indiana, united to enhance pharmacists' ability to provide pharmaceutical care and to further the public's recognition of the profession's value. One can imagine that if the figures from the association's history could have leapt off the pages of the journals, they would have stared across the meeting room proud of the 125 years of accomplishments and given their fellow pharmacists an affirmative nod for a job well done, with confidence in their continuing future success.

Section 5 Endnotes

1 "Effort to 'build a home for pharmacy' begins", *The Indiana Pharmacist*, 70 no. 5 (1989), 6.

2 "President's Message", *The Indiana Pharmacist*, 71 no. 9 (1990), 5.

3 "Welcome Lary Sage New IPA Executive Vice President Named", *The Indiana Pharmacist*, 72 no. 4 (1991), 9.

4 "Many Thanks to Joseph E. McSoley, P.D.", *The Indiana Pharmacist*, 72 no. 4 (1991), 9.

5 "Joseph E. McSoley, P.D. Receives the 1991 Sperandio Award", *The Indiana Pharmacist*, 72 no. 5 (1991), 7.

6 "Remembering Joe…", *The Indiana Pharmacist*, 77 no. 5 (1991), 12.

7 "Sage Advice", *The Indiana Pharmacist*, 78 no. 4 (1997), 6.

8 "Alliance Activities", *The Indiana Pharmacist*, 78 no. 6 (1997), 4.

9 "First Annual Indiana Pharmacists Alliance Annual Meeting", *The Indiana Pharmacist*, 49 no. 2 (1998), 8.

Appendices

Indiana Pharmacists Alliance
PRESIDENT INDEX

Indiana Pharmacists Association 1882-1997

1882	G. H. ANDREWS	Muncie
1883	N. W. YEAKLE	Lafayette
1884	W. L. JOHNSTON	Evansville
1885	A. J. DETZER	Ft. Wayne
1886	LEO ELIEL	South Bend
1887	D. W. BRYANT	Frankfort
1888	ARTHUR L. GREEN	Lafayette
1889	ALBERT ALLEN	Greencastle
1890	JOHN N. HURTY	Indianapolis
1891	W. C. BUNTON	Terre Haute
1892	FRANK H. CARTER	Indianapolis
1893	JOHN KENNEDY	Vincennes
1894	GEORGE W. HAYNIE	Evansville
1895	THOMAS J. MOFFAT	Edinburg
1896	WILLIAM O. GROSS	Ft. Wayne
1897	R. I. EADS	Indianapolis
1898	F. H. BURTON	Evansville
1899	F. D. WARNER	New Castle
1900	FRED W. MEISSNER	LaPorte
1901	CHARLES O. PRUTZMAN	Muncie
1902	OTTO C. BASTIAN	South Bend
1903	MARION A. STOUT	Bluffton
1904	CASSIUS E. ELLIOTT	Sheridan
1905	HARRY E. GLICK	Lafayette
1906	BRUNO KNOEFEL	New Albany
1907	LOUIS TEEPE	Evansville
1908	E. W. STUCKY	Indianapolis
1909	BURTON CASSADAY	Terre Haute
1910	ROSCOE MUTZ	Edinburg
1911	T. C. BAYSE	Rockport
1912	CHARLES A. HAUPT	Terre Haute
1913	C. L. HACKETT	Roanoke
1914	ERNEST H. W. STAHLHUTH	Columbus
1915	CHARLES GENOLEN	Nashville
1916	M. A. STOUT	Bluffton
1917	W. H. RUDDER	Salem
1918	E. W. STUCKY	Indianapolis
1919	E. W. MAY	Martinsville
1920	T. B. CRIGLER	Attica
1921	B. M. KEENE	Indianapolis
1922	WILLIAM F. WERNER	Indianapolis
1923	JOSEPH H. WEIS	Hammond
1924	SCOTT KELLY	Gaston
1925	EARL E. GOODNIGHT	Lafayette
1926	HERMAN BILL	Ft. Wayne
1927	WOOD WILES	Bloomington
1928	L. B. UPTON	Evansville
1929	C. E. NELSON	Hammond
1930	ROBERT I. BEDDOE	Beford
1931	LAWSON A. COOKE	Goodland
1932	FRANCIS A. BRITT	Evansville
1933	ASA SMITH	Logansport
1934	E. A. RIDGELY	Gary
1934	ED N. HARPER	Muncie
1935	HARRY W. MILLER	Terre Haute
1936	A. J. DOUGHERTY	South Bend
1937	KEIFER ELLIOTT	Sheridan
1938	H. H. GERDING	Ft. Wayne
1939	JOSEPH B. WADE	Indianapolis
1940	IRA ROTHROCK	Mount Vernon
1941	CHARLES D. SCHREIBER	Tell City
1942	STEPHEN BADANISH	Gary
1943	STEPHEN BADANISH	Gary
1944	CECIL GOUGH	Hartford City
1945	CECIL GOUGH	Hartford City
1946	GORDON A. TRIPLETT	Osgood
1947	LAWRENCE C. HEUSTIS	Indianapolis
1948	M. MAURICE GOODNIGHT	Lafayette
1949	WILFRID J. ULLRICH	Aurora
1950	FRED E. THOMAS	Greenfield
1951	EMERY A. BADANISH	Gary
1952	BYRON CHILDRESS	Mishawaka
1953	A. T. EHRHARDT	Kokomo
1954	FRANK LOBRAICO	Indianapolis
1955	ORGLE E. MYERS	Boonville
1956	IVAN W. HOLDER	Monticello
1957	ROBERT C. HEIKOWSKY	Ft. Wayne
1958	KENNETH B. LAMONT	South Bend
1959	O. E. HINSHAW	Elwood
1960	GEORGE M. LANIGAN	Indianapolis
1961	DONALD N. WOOD	Evansville
1962	EARL G. TRIPLETT	Osgood

1963	MERRITT L. SKINNER	Plymouth
1964	CHARLES A. SCHREIBER	Tell City
1965	THURMAN H. MILLER	Terre Haute
1966	ROY W. HANEY	Muncie
1967	JOSEPH E. McSOLEY	Indianapolis
1968	WILLIAM L. LONG	Lafayette
1969	COURTLAND DRIGGS	Hammond
1970	WILLIAM A. ARLAND	Shelbyville
1971	FRANK C. FITCH	Delphi
1972	RICHARD H. DEARDORFF	Mishawaka
1973	CHARLES THURGOOD	Evansville
1974	DALE DOERR	Indianapolis
1975	LEROY RHEA	Muncie
1976	BARBARA A. NELSON	Lafayette
1977	RALPH E. ANDERSON	Bedford
1978	MELVIN LICHTENFELD	Crown Point
1979	JAMES R. SMITH	Indianapolis
1980	DONALD L. MOORE	Kokomo
1981	ROBERT WITTGEN	Evansville
1982	LYNN OATES	Floyd Knobs
1983	RICHARD BRYCHELL	Valparaiso
1984	WARREN HICKMAN	Paris
1985	CHESTER FREELAND	Plainfield
1986	ROBERT SCOTT	Columbus
1987	JOHN GAULT	South Bend
1988	CYNTHIA WEIL	Evansville
1989	DENNIS MCCALLIAN	West Lafayette
1990	RHONDA ELDRIDGE	Connersville
1991	CHARLES DOBIS	South Bend
1992	WINIFRED LANDIS	Lafayette
1993	LLOYD CLAYBAUGH	Evansville
1994	BRUCE HUFFORD	West Lafayette
1995	LEROY RHEA II	Muncie
1996	JOSEPH LUGAR	Terre Haute
1997	BRUCE CLAYTON	Carmel

Indiana Pharmacists Alliance - 1998–present

1998	BRUCE CLAYTON	Carmel
1999	FRANCINE BRECKLER	Indianapolis
2000	MICHAEL SIEVERS	Leo
2001	BRUCE CARLSTEDT	Westfield
2002	KEN HURLESS	Newburgh
2003	DAWN BLANK	Indianapolis
2004	VAL BERGER	Carmel
2005	WILLIAM MALLOY	Avon
2006	PATRICK CASHEN	Columbus
2007	TOM FITE	Evansville

Indiana Pharmacists Alliance - Executive Directors

1882-1886
Joseph R. Perry, Indianapolis

1886-1887
Frank S. Hereth ,Indianapolis

1887-1891
Joseph R. Perry ,Indianapolis

1891-1893
Fred W. Meissner ,LaPorte

1893-1895
William A. Stocker ,Indianapolis

1895-1908
A. W. Timberlake ,Indianapolis

1908-1915
M. P. Schwartz ,Indianapolis

1915-1919
William F. Werner ,Indianapolis

1919-1927
William A. Oren ,Indianapolis

1927-1938*
Frank V. McCullough ,New Albany

1938-1939
Joseph L. Weinland ,Brazil

1939-1948
Harold V. Darnell ,Indianapolis

1948-1959
Henry W. Heine ,Indianapolis

1959-1964
Lawrence C. Heustis, Indianapolis

1964-1970
James D. Hawkins, Indianapolis

1970-1991
David A. Clark, Plainfield

1991-present
Lawrence J. Sage, Noblesville

* In 1927 the Executive Director became a full-time position

Past IPA Award Recipients

Last Updated 7/23/07

IPA ANNUAL COLLEGE BOWL

1997 – Purdue University

1998 – Butler University

1999 – Butler University

2000 – Butler University

2003 – Butler University

College Bowl Suspended

IPA OUTSTANDING PHARMACY TECHNICIAN OF THE YEAR

1998 – Jan M. Henline

1999 – Debra Hewson

2000 – Jenny Byard

2001 – Georgia Wagers

2002 – Rob France

2003 – Trela J. Malone

2004 – Kimberly M. Jones

2005 – Teresa Pionke

2006 – Michael Motley

IPA OUTSTANDING STUDENT OF THE YEAR

1992 – Sarah Wassmuth, Purdue University

1993 – Rose Olson, Purdue University

1993 – Amy Novina, Butler University

1994 – Denise Dobek, Purdue University

1994 – Dawn Blank, Purdue University

1997 – Cynthia Ross, Purdue University

2000 – Sarah Myers, Butler University

2001 – Sam Lee, Butler University

2002 – Britta Penn, Purdue University

2003 – Leroy Rhea III, Butler University

2003 – Joel Light, Purdue University

2004 – Cheryl Guzikowski, Purdue University

2005 – Vyto Damasius, Purdue University

2006 – Mark Brown, Purdue University

APOTHECON PAST PRESIDENT'S AWARD – ALLIANCE

1997 – Joseph J. Lugar, Association

1998 – Bruce D. Clayton, Alliance

1998 – Bruce C. Carlstedt, ISHP

1999 – Francine D. Breckler, Alliance

2000 – Michael A. Sievers, Alliance

2001 – Bruce C. Carlstedt, Alliance

2002 – Kenneth L. Hurless

2003 – Dawn Blank

2004 – James V. (Val) Berger

2005 – William X. Malloy

2006 – Patrick J. Cashen

ELAN (DUPONT) INNOVATIVE PHARMACY PRACTICE AWARD

1997 – Janice C. Bopp

1998 – Suellyn J. Sorensen

1999 – Charles A. Lindstrom

2000 – Judy Bennett

2001 – Misty Abrams

Company changed name to ELAN

2002 – Brian Newton

2003 – Daniel D. Degnan

2004 – Jamie Vortherms

2005 – Edward Walker

2006 – Thomas Miller

GLEN SPERANDIO HEALTH-SYSTEM PHARMACIST OF THE YEAR

1998 – Michael A. Sievers, R.Ph.

1999 – Francine D. Breckler, Pharm.D.

2000 – Kenneth L. Hurless, R.Ph.

2001 – Jennifer McComb, Pharm.D.

2002 – Daniel D. Degnan, Pharm.D.

2003 – Suellyn Sorenson, Pharm.D.

2004 – Julie Everett, Pharm.D.

2005 – Jim H. Seibert, R.Ph

2006 – William X. Malloy, Pharm.D.

JOSEPH E. MCSOLEY PHARMACIST OF THE YEAR

1986 – Joseph E. McSoley

1987 – Stephen W. Schondelmeyer

1988 – John D. Gerhart

1989 – Marvin D. Riegsecker

1990 – Thomas J. Meier

1991 – Thurman Miller

1992 – Leroy E. Rhea

1993 – Donald Moore

1994 – Charles G. Dobis

1995 – Frank C. Fitch

1996 – Winnie Landis

1997 – Bruce A. Hufford, R.Ph.

1998 – George S. Kucka, R.Ph.

1999 – Maurice A. Keltsch, R.Ph.

2000 – Charles Thurgood, R.Ph.

2001 – Barbara A. Nelson, R.Ph.

2002 – Melvin Lichtenfeld, R.Ph.

2003 – Patrick Cashen, R.Ph.

2004 – Marc O. Merrill, R.Ph.

2005 – Christine Farnham, R.Ph.

2006 – Kipland J. Burkett, R.Ph.

JOSEPH E. MCSOLEY SCHOLARSHIP

1998 – Jason E. Streit, Butler University
1998 – Nathan W. Gabhart, Purdue University
1999 – Laura Opincar, Butler University
1999 – Kimberly A. Siewert, Purdue University
2000 – Kara Birrer, Butler University
2001 – Leroy E. Rhea III, Butler University
2001 – Angie A. Steinhardt, Purdue University
2002 – Leroy E. Rhea III, Butler University
2002 – Jennifer A. Gatsos, Purdue University
2003 – Eric Smith, Purdue University
2003 – Melissa Allard, Butler University
2004 – Patrick Lai, Butler University
2004 – Wesley McMillian, Purdue University
2005 – Courtney Sheehan, Butler University
2005 – Gene Rhea, Purdue University
2006 – Lindsay Whisenant, Butler University
2006 – Vyto Damasius, Purdue University

MERCK ACHIEVEMENT AWARD (OUTGOING PRESIDENT)

1998 – Bruce D. Clayton
1999 – Francine D. Breckler
2000 – Michael A. Sievers
2001 – Bruce C. Carlstedt
2002 – Kenneth L. Hurless
2003 – Dawn Blank
2004 – James V. (Val) Berger
2005 – William X. Malloy
2006 – Patrick J. Cashen

NCPA PHARMACY LEADERSHIP AWARD (INCOMING PRESIDENT'S PLAQUE)

1994 – Bruce A. Hufford
1997 – Bruce D. Clayton
1998 – Francine D. Breckler
1999 – Michael A. Sievers
2000 – Bruce C. Carlstedt
2001 – Kenneth L. Hurless
2002 – Dawn Blank
2003 – James V. (Val) Berger
2004 – William X. Malloy
2005 – Patrick J. Cashen
2006 – Thomas C. Fite

PHARMACISTS MUTUAL INSURANCE COMPANIES DISTINGUISHED YOUNG PHARMACIST AWARD

(formerly presented by Marion Merrell Dow)

1997 – Dawn Blank
1998 – Tina Bauman
1999 – Julie A. Everett
2000 – Daniel D. Degnan
2001 – Jennifer S. McComb
2002 – Niki Gish-Morrow
2003 – Lauren Angelo
2004 – Scott B. Hufford
2005 – Amanda Quebe
2006 – Carriann E. Richey

PRESIDENT'S AWARD OF APPRECIATION

1997 – Sen. Potch Wheeler
1997 – Rep. Matt Whetstone
1998 – Knoll Pharmaceutical
1999 – Rep. Peggy Welch
1999 – G. Thomas Wilson

WYETH BOWL OF HYGEIA AWARD

1963 – H. George Dekay
1964 – Avery E. Deupree
1965 – Wilfrid J. Ullrich
1966 – H. Alexander Woods
1967 – Denis E. Ribordy
1968 – Robert S. Hutto
1969 – Leroy E. Rhea
1970 – Donald M. Newman
1971 – Joseph E. Mcsoley
1972 – William L. Long
1973 – James G. Walters
1974 – Charles A. Schreiber, Sr.
1975 – Frank C. Fitch
1976 – Ralph E. Anderson
1977 – Cortland S. Driggs
1978 – Bruce A. Hufford
1979 – David A. Clark
1980 – Melvin A. Lichtenfeld
1981 – Barbara A. Nelson
1982 – John P. Gault
1983 – Eward W. Stoltz
1984 – Donald L. Moore
1985 – Thurman H. Miller
1986 – Dennis J. McCallian
1987 – Richard S. Brychell
1988 – Max A. Cowan
1989 – Charles H. Thurgood
1990 – John D. Gerhart
1991 – Gary E. Jacobi
1992 – Cynthia A. Weil
1993 – Thomas J. Meier
1994 – J. Bruce Laughrey
1995 – Robert A. Chalmers
1996 – Robert A. Sandmann
1997 – Bruce C. Carlstedt
1998 – Winnie Landis
1999 – Lloyd J. Claybaugh
2000 – Robert E. Deremiah
2001 – Donna S. Wall
2002 – Bruce D. Clayton
2003 – James E. Berger
2004 – Carol Birk
2005 – John A. Cowan
2006 – Christine Farnham

Indiana Pharmacists
LEADERS OF NATIONAL PHARMACY ORGANIZATIONS

American Pharmaceutical Association/American Pharmacists Association
1. George Wilson Sloan, Indianapolis, President, 1879-80
2. Leo Eliel, South Bend, President, 1906-07
3. Winnie Landis, Lafayette, President, 2007-08

American Pharmaceutical Association/American Pharmacists Association Foundation
1. Joe McSoley, Indianapolis, President, 1979-90

American Society of Hospital Pharmacists
1. Allen V.R. Crum, President, 1954

National Association of Retail Druggists/National Community Pharmacists Association
1. M.A. Stout...Bluffton...1915-16
2. William Oren...Indianapolis...1927-28
3. Albert Fritz...Indianapolis...1939-40
4. Frank Lobraico...Indianapolis...1962-63
5. Donald Moore...Kokomo...1992-93

National Council of State Pharmacy Association Executives
1. F.V. McCullough, President, 1934-35
2. David A. Clark, President, 1975-76

National Association of Boards of Pharmacy
1. Donna Wall, Indianapolis, President 2003-2004.

Sources Consulted and Further Reading

Books

Anderson, Ann, *Snake Oil, Hustlers and Hambones: The American Medicine Show.* Jefferson, NC: McFarland &Company, Inc., 2000.

Eckles, Robert B., *Purdue Pharmacy: The First Century.* West Lafayette: Purdue Research Foundation, 1979.

Gould, Lewis L., America in the Progressive Era: 1890 -1914. New York: Longman, 2001.

Hilts, Philip J., *Protecting America's Health: The FDA, Business, and One Hundred Years of Regulation.* Chapel Hill: UNC Press, 2004.

Madison, James H., *The Indiana Way: A State History.* Bloomington: Indiana University Press, 1990.

Madison, James H., *Eli Lilly: A Life, 1885 – 1977.* Bloomington: Indiana University Press, 1989.

Porter, Roy, *The Greatest Benefit to Mankind: A Medical History of Humanity.* New York: W.W. Norton & Company, 1997.

Shorter, Edward, *The Health Century.* New York: Doubleday, 1987.

Young, James Harvey, *The Toadstool Millionaires: A social History of Patent Medicines before Federal Regulation.* New Jersey: Princeton University Press, 1961.

Journals and Meeting Proceedings

The Indiana Pharmacist, 1882 – present.

The Proceedings of the Indiana Pharmaceutical Association, 1882 – 1916.

The Monthly Bulletin of the Indiana State Board of Health, 1899 – 1965.